PROPERTY OF W9-DCY-161

ENGINEERING DEPT.

RETURN TO FILE OF MR CARROLL

463

WELD
DESIGN

WELD

DESIGN

HARRY D. CHURCHILL

PROFESSOR OF ENGINEERING MECHANICS
CASE INSTITUTE OF TECHNOLOGY

JOHN B. AUSTIN

WELDING ENGINEER
REPUBLIC STRUCTURAL IRON WORKS

NEW YORK

PRENTICE-HALL, INC.

1949

PRINTED IN THE UNITED STATES OF AMERICA

Preface

Weld Design is intended to supply a definite need for a concise volume on welded machine-base design. Machine-design textbooks have thoroughly described the design of cast machine bases, but very little information has been available with regard to the welded type of base. The reason for this situation is, of course, that electric arc welding is a production tool that only in recent years has been developed to the point, both metallurgically and in a manufacturing sense, where it has been generally recognized by the machine designer. Today the process of fabricating machine bases by arc welding is being applied to many different types of designs, and selection is made on the basis of sound engineering and economy. Many engineers are aware of these advances but in many instances are unable to proceed because of a lack of welding-design experience and information.

At the outset the authors recognized that, in order to supply the needed information, this volume should treat the subject of design from both the practical and theoretical standpoints. Furthermore, they felt that the designer should have a thorough understanding of the materials that enter into machine-base construction and a clear picture of the many methods of processing plates and structural shapes. Economical welding design is largely dependent on a proper choice of components.

The designer should understand the fabrication methods of the modern weldery and the essential processes of welding and flame cutting. He is chiefly concerned, however, with the amount and the type of welding that go into the structure, leaving it to the weldery to carry out the details in accomplishing the result. The authors have avoided going into great detail on the subject of welding technique, and they suggest that a welding manual be consulted for such information.

Appendix II, a comprehensive list of magazine articles, pamphlets, and books bearing upon the subject of welded-machine design and related matter, has been drawn upon freely in the preparation of this text.

Thanks is extended to friends who kindly furnished drawings and photographs and who offered valuable criticism.

HARRY D. CHURCHILL

JOHN B. AUSTIN

Cleveland, Ohio

Contents

CHAPTER I

Introduction

Machine, Machine Base, and Weldment

A *machine* is defined as any device consisting of two or more resistant, relatively constrained parts that may serve to transmit and modify force and motion so as to do some desired kind of work. The popular conception of a machine also includes the framework and the attachments.

Any structure that serves as the sole support for either a single machine unit or for a combination of machine units is defined as a *machine base*. As an example, the usual mounting for a motor generator set is a low type of base generally referred to as a motor base or a machine base. The term "machine base," is also used to describe the supporting structure for a Diesel or gas engine. The most common usage of the term is in conjunction with machine tools.

The term "weldment" applies to any assembly of metal parts that is fabricated by welding. A welded machine base is a weldment, but a weldment is not necessarily a machine base. It may be a roof truss, a tank, or other assembly having no connection with machinery.

The principal function of a machine base is to retain the mechanical movements of the machinery in proper working relationship. Consequently, the structure must be rigid, and the deflections must be held within permissible limits. In order to design a base for a new-type machine to meet these conditions, it is necessary first to analyze and estimate the static and dynamic stresses that will be present in the base structure. The most efficient shapes and materials must then be combined to resist these stresses. In addition to meeting these physical requirements, the design must conform to the strictest rules of economy in order that the finished product may meet price competition.

The Stress-Analysis Problem

There are two general types of machine-base design problems. The first concerns the common box or platform structure that merely *supports* a fixed or moving load. In such a structure the stresses are simple, and the maximum loading is readily determined. Therefore, the frame members and the stiffening ribs can be accurately designed to resist such stresses and confine the deflections to the limits established in the initial requirements of the problem. Examples of this type of machine base are the drilling machine, planer, surface-grinding machine, and the hobbing machine.

In the second type of problem, the machine base not only *supports* the working members of the machine but is also *subject to the major working stresses*. These are frequently so complicated and various that it is impossible to make an exact analysis. In such cases, the main stresses are determined as accurately as possible, and suitable allowance is made in the stiffness of the design to provide a sufficient factor of safety. The design data should be thoroughly checked by making an experimental machine model and submitting it to a complete service test before the design is accepted. Machine tools such as shears and presses are in this classification. In highly stressed machine frames of certain types, it is impossible for the design to accommodate all possible contingencies. The frame takes care of normal operating stresses plus some overload. Beyond this point, safety control devices protect the frame from failure. For example, in a press brake driven by a flywheel, the energy of the stroke (determined by the weight of the flywheel and its speed of rotation) is constant as long as the ram moves downward at a uniform rate. If there is a resistance to this free movement of the ram due to excessive resistance to deformation of the material being worked, the overload is directly transmitted to the stress members of the frame and may reach high limits. It is impossible to estimate the maximum stresses that may be reached under such conditions. They readily attain a degree of overload that may cause distortion or failure of the structural members. This condition is taken care of by providing a liberal factor of safety and some overload safety release device.

Selection of Material and Construction Method

In close conjunction with the study and analysis of the working stresses in a particular machine base, it is necessary to choose the most efficient and economical material and method of construction. A thorough understanding of the properties of the various metals commonly used in such construction is essential in order to utilize the selected process to the fullest extent. The nature and magnitude of the stresses in a machine base may be such as to fix definitely the type of metal best suited for the structure. The choice of a certain metal may also establish the process best suited.

The following are the metals and methods commonly employed in machine-base construction:

Casting process
1. Ordinary gray iron
2. Alloyed iron
3. Steel

Fabrication of rolled steel by arc welding
1. Low-carbon hot-rolled steel
2. Low-alloy high-strength steel
3. 40–50 carbon steel

Methods of Construction

Until recent years, the casting process was the traditional method used in the manufacture of machine bases. Knowledge of cast-iron design has been handed down through the years; the principles and the methods have both been standardized and are well known, and there is very little that can be added to existing knowledge.[1]

On the other hand, the electric arc-welding process of fabricating machine bases of hot-rolled steel is relatively new and possesses

---

[1] For additional information, the reader is referred to (1) *Cast Metals Handbook,* American Foundrymen's Association, Chicago, Ill., 1944 ed.; (2) *Foundrymen's Handbook,* 1st ed., Penton Publishing Co., Cleveland, Ohio, 1923.

many advantages over former methods of construction,[2] such as light weight, simplicity of design, strength, rigidity, good performance, and low cost. To make full use of these advantages, the designer requires much detailed information.

Welding fabrication is revolutionary in its departure from the old rules and restrictions of casting. The welding process is extremely flexible; metals of any thickness and shape are joined. The structure may consist of many components such as sheared and cut shapes, bent shapes, oxyacetylene cut shapes, rolled sections, forgings, and stampings, piping, and steel castings. The composition and the physical properties of these components may vary over a wide range. There is great latitude in the selection and location of a component part in the structure. The only restrictions are the manufacturing limits in processing the various components. The economy in welded design is developed first by understanding the many details of the welding process, and secondly by employing ingenuity in simple designs and layouts.

---

[2] In a paper presented before the American Iron and Steel Institute in 1933, H. G. Marsh of the Carnegie Steel Company said: "A striking change has come over the modern machine shop. Scattered throughout are numerous lights; some are bluish, sputtering ones of great intensity with hooded ghoulish figures attending them. Others are bright yellow throwing off at times showers of sparks. These lights mark a new era in machine construction, for two new fabricating processes have been introduced into the industry—flame-cutting and welding. These processes have in turn introduced a new type of construction and a new material, rolled steel."

CHAPTER 2

Construction Materials of Machine Bases

Choice of Material

Engineering is defined by Webster as "the art and science by which the properties of matter and the sources of power in nature are made useful to man in structure, machines, and manufactured products." In the design of machine bases, the properties of the material have great bearing on the size, shape, weight, performance, and cost of the finished structure. The engineer studies such properties as the tensile and compressive strength, ductility, yield point, specific gravity, endurance limit, impact resistance, stiffness, machinability, and hardness. He is particularly interested in the relationship between these properties and their effect upon the design. In many cases, a proper choice cannot be made until an actual design, based upon a thorough understanding of the materials, has been prepared.

Progress in any engineering field is the result of research and intelligent application of the principles developed. The engineer is constantly searching for better materials and at the same time is concerned with the selection of the best material available at the time for a given application. Steel is selected for the automobile body because it combines maximum strength and resistance to vibration, shock, and other stresses with fairly light weight and minimum cost. For the small-engine cylinder block, which is subject to high temperature and corrosion and is of an intricate shape with many passages and openings, cast iron is excellent from both the engineering and cost standpoints. In machine design, the engineer carefully selects the best material for the gears, cams, valves, bearings, shafts, and other components. Likewise, in view

5

of the present knowledge of constructing machinery bases, the designer must make a choice between casting and welding fabrication; his decision should be based upon sound engineering principles and cost.

Ordinary Open-grained Gray-Iron Castings

Ordinary gray-iron castings are made in accordance with American Society for Testing Materials (A.S.T.M.) specification A48–36:

COMPOSITION OF OPEN-GRAINED
GRAY-IRON CASTINGS

Alloy Metal	Per Cent
Carbon	2.80–3.80
Silicon	1.20–2.60
Manganese	0.50–1.00
Sulphur	0.90–0.12
Phosphorus	0.50 max.

The term "ordinary" is generally used to designate that no special alloys are present to increase the tensile properties of the iron. Ordinary gray iron may be described as steel broken up by flakes of free carbon or graphite. The amount of graphite flakes present depends upon the composition and the rate of cooling. The steel content will vary in composition, ranging from an almost carbon-free state to the strongest or fully pearlitic state with the carbon content at about 0.8 per cent.

Gray iron is not a homogeneous material; the microstructure will vary in different parts of the casting, depending upon the cooling rate. The size and location of the ribs and sections as well as the pouring gates all affect the physical properties and the microstructure.

The presence of free graphite and the general lack of homogeneity account for three of the special characteristics of gray-iron castings—good lubrication, wearing, and dampening. Good lubrication and wearing properties are attributed to the fact that the porousness, thanks to the presence of free graphite, results in the absorption and retention of large quantities of oil that lubricate the wearing surfaces. It is easy to hand-scrape the slideways, which provide good wearing surfaces. Good dampening characteristics are also attributed to the lack of uniformity in the material and to the fact that the vibrations are interrupted rather than transmitted through it.

Some of the difficulties associated with the casting process are porosity and slag inclusions. Porosity may be a serious matter if it is detected in a large casting after considerable machining has been done. Also, inequalities in the wall thickness of a casting sometimes result from movement of the core in pouring, thereby creating an unbalanced structure.

Gray-iron castings develop internal stresses in cooling because of inequalities in the cooling rate of different parts of the casting that vary in thickness. Such stresses will cause the casting to creep when machined. If the rough casting is exposed to atmospheric temperature for a long period, usually six months or more, the stresses will be relieved. This procedure is known as *air-seasoning* or *aging*. The rush of business usually demands a more rapid practice, so it is customary to relieve the stresses by heat-treatment, in which the castings are heated throughout to a temperature of 950° F. and then slowly cooled in the furnace. Drastic machining operations will also cause internal stresses and creepage. In machining parts for precision machinery, it is customary to take a rough cut, then heat-treat, and finally finish with the smooth final cut. Heat-treatment is also used to decrease the hardness of cast iron and to improve the machinability. There are also cases where the hardness is increased by heat-treatment.

The cost of castings is closely associated with the cost of the pattern and the number of castings produced. The pattern cost may be a major factor if only one or a few castings are produced but is of little consequence with many castings of one kind. Where many different types and sizes of castings are produced, the matter of pattern cost, inventory, and storage may all be major considerations.

In physical properties, ordinary gray iron has low tensile strength, low resistance to fatigue and impact, and practically no ductility. Its modulus of elasticity is low and its compressive strength high in comparison with those of steel. The compressive strength is four to five times as great as the tensile strength. In addition, this material is very resistant to corrosion and scaling at high temperatures.

Alloy Cast Iron

Alloy iron castings are made in accordance with the A.S.T.M. Specification A48–36:

COMPOSITION OF ALLOY CAST IRON

Alloy Metal	Per Cent
Carbon	2.80–3.80
Silicon	1.20–2.60
Manganese	0.50–1.00
Sulphur	0.09–0.12
Phosphorus	0.50 max.
Nickel	0.50–3.00
Chromium	0.20–0.60
Molybdenum	0.25–0.50

"Alloy cast iron" refers to plain cast iron with the addition of the elements nickel, chromium, and molybdenum, either singly or in combination. These additions are made essentially to increase the tensile strength and modulus of elasticity. Improvement in density is also obtained. Nickel is similar to silicon in promoting the formation of free graphite. Chromium is added because it is a good carbide former, thereby increasing the hardening capacity of the iron. Chromium carbides are also more sensitive to chill than other carbides. Nickel and chromium are often used together to improve the structure and to increase the tensile strength and the hardness without impairing the machinability of the metal. Molybdenum, the most efficient alloy material for increasing strength, is added for this purpose and to bring about higher density and structural uniformity.

Alloys increase the cost considerably, particularly in large castings. This extra cost must be justified through improved physical properties and their effect on the design of the structure.

Alloy cast irons for machine tools commonly have a tensile range of 25,000 to 45,000 lb. per square inch (p.s.i.), though heat-treatment may be used to increase this strength up to 65,000 p.s.i. The modulus of elasticity of the alloy casting is greatly increased over that of the ordinary gray-iron casting but not in proportion to the increase in tensile strength; it ranges between 11,000,000 for weak irons and 22,000,000 for high-strength irons.

The dampening capacity of alloy cast iron decreases as the tensile strength and modulus of elasticity increase. It is customary for some designers to accept a compromise in composition.

The wearing resistance of cast iron is increased by the addition of alloys, though this increase is not sufficient for precision work where a hard wearing surface is required. This is obtained by using chilling plates in the mold adjacent to the ways and wearing surfaces, or by flame-hardening the wearing surfaces. As has been mentioned, chromium is highly beneficial in promoting the hardness in this manner. An alloy iron of 2 to 3 per cent nickel and 0.5 per cent chromium will give a Brinell hardness of 250 to 300 as cast. It can be oil-quenched from 850° F. to give a final hardness of 350 to 450 Brinell. The surface should then be ground to a finish.

Meehanite [1]

Meehanite is a metallurgically processed cast material rigidly controlled in metal structure rather than in chemical composition, as is common in iron-foundry practice. Ordinary cast iron consists of about 53.7 per cent pearlite, 26.11 per cent silica ferrite, 10.15 per cent graphite, and 10.0 per cent iron phosphide. Meehanite grade GA consists of 91.5 per cent pearlite, 7.25 per cent graphite, and 1.25 per cent iron phosphide. Its physical properties are listed in Table 2–1 on page 10.

A fine equiaxed grain structure is obtained, which accounts for the high strength and toughness of the metal. Meehanite is manufactured to a large number of specifications for many purposes. The GA grade is recommended for general engineering work.

Welding Cast Iron

When gray iron is melted, the free graphite goes back into solution. A rapid quench produces white cast iron, which is hard and brittle. All methods of welding cast iron are designed to avoid or minimize this formation of a brittle constituent in the weld zone. Although cast iron is often welded in the repair and salvage of castings, it cannot be considered a weldable material in the sense that steel and other commonly welded metals are, because of the extra caution required and the relatively high cost and greater time for making a production weld.

The following successful methods of welding gray cast iron are also applicable to Meehanite and alloy cast iron.

(1) *The cast-iron weld.* The casting is preheated with a kerosene or oxyacetylene torch to a dull red. A cast-iron rod with a high

---

[1] See "Meehanite Metal," Meehanite Metal Corp., Pittsburgh.

TABLE 2-1: COMPARISON OF IMPORTANT FERROUS METALS USED IN MACHINE-BASE CONSTRUCTION

Property	Cast				Rolled		
	Ordinary open-grained gray iron	Alloy gray iron	Meehanite* Grade GA	Cast steel A: As Cast B: Annealed C: Quench and Temper	Hot-rolled low-carbon steel	Grade A low-alloy high-strength steel	Grade B low-alloy high-strength steel
Ultimate tensile strength, p.s.i.	15,000 to 25,000	Up to 70,000	Over 50,000	A: 65,000 B: 70,000 C: 80,000	55,000 to 65,000	70,000 to 80,000	90,000 to 100,000
Percentage, elongation in 2 in.	None	None	None	A: 20 B: 30 C: 20	30–40	25–30	15–20
Percentage reduction of area	None	None	None	A: 30 B: 45 C: 30	60–70	50–60	45–50
Density, lb. per cu. ft.	450	450	450	A: 480 B: 480 C: 480	480	480	480
Endurance limit, p s.i.	6,000 to 10,000	Up to 22,000	22,000		26,000 to 32,000	45,000	57,000
Brinell hardness	120 to 190	180 to 270	207 and up	A: 140 B: 130 C: 160	120	130	160
Yield strength, p.s.i.	15,000 to 19,000	Up to 45,000	45,000	A: 35,000 B: 40,000 C: 50,000	30,000 to 35,000	50,000 to 60,000	60,000 to 68,000
Modulus of elasticity	12,000,000	Up to 22,000,000	21,000,000	30,000,000	30,000,000	30,000,000	30,000,000
Corrosion	Superior to steel (L.C.)	Superior to steel (L.C.)	Superior to steel (L.C.)			Superior to steel (L.C.)	Superior to steel (L.C.)
Shearing strength, p.s.i.	27,000 to 35,000	45,000 to 60,000	48,000	A: 52,000 B: 56,000 C: 64,000	45,000 to 52,000	56,000 to 64,000	72,000 to 80,000
Machinability	Superior to steel (L.C.)	Superior to steel (L.C.)	Superior to steel (L.C.)				
Compressive strength, p.s.i.	90,000	Up to 175,000	175,000	A: 35,000 B: 40,000 C: 50,000	45,000 to 52,000	56,000 to 64,000	72,000 to 80,000

10

silicon content, to promote the formation of free graphite in the deposit, is melted into the groove by means of the carbon arc or the oxyacetylene flame. The casting is then covered with asbestos and allowed to cool slowly. Although this is the best type of weld for cast iron, it is slow and expensive. The weld metal has qualities similar to the casting after proper preheating and slow cooling and is machinable.

(2) *The bronze weld.* A common type of weld is the brazed joint. The members are vee'd and preheated to a dull-red heat. The weld is made with a bronze rod using the oxyacetylene torch and a good brazing compound. After the weld is completed, the joint is permitted to cool. This weld is satisfactory because of the low brazing temperature and the shallow fusion zone in the parent metal. The bronze deposit is unaltered by the parent metal and remains ductile and strong.

(3) *The monel metal weld.* Monel metal is a copper-nickel alloy. Neither constituent will absorb carbon. An electrode coated with monel metal is deposited on cast iron with the electric arc and produces a machinable weld down to the fused cast-iron zone. The shallow penetration of the electrode minimizes the formation of white cast iron.

(4) *The mild-steel weld.* A weld made with an ordinary mild-steel electrode in cast iron may crack or peel away from the parent metal because of the higher shrinkage characteristic of the steel deposit. This difficulty is avoided by using steel studs that act as tie-downs for the weld metal and maintain a mechanical bond between the two metals. Special mild-steel electrodes have been developed with special coatings that permit the use of low currents and tend to form a sound bond with the casting with minimum penetration. The first layer of weld metal is hard and brittle, but successive layers are soft and ductile. Satisfactory welds are made without the use of studs.

Malleable-Iron Castings

Malleable-iron castings are manufactured from white cast iron by a long annealing process that gives the casting greater tensile strength, ductility, and resistance to shock than can be obtained in gray iron. Whenever malleable iron is fused as in welding, the metal reverts to white cast iron, which is hard and brittle. Steel pipe fittings are used in preference to malleable fittings in fabricated bases requiring welded connections and joints.

Malleable-iron castings are made in accordance with A.S.T.M. Specification A47–33:

PROPERTIES OF MALLEABLE CAST IRON

Property	Grade 32510	Grade 35018
Tensile strength (p.s.i.)	50,000	53,000
Yield point (p.s.i.)	32,000	35,000
Elongation (in./2 in.)	10%	18%

Cast Steel

The steel casting was born out of the necessity for a material of superior physical, thermal, and corrosion-resisting properties and capable of being cast into intricate shapes.

There are two general types of steel castings: carbon-steel and alloy-steel. The bulk of the castings produced in the United States are of the carbon-steel type and conform to the following analysis:

COMPOSITION OF CAST STEEL

Alloy Metal	Per Cent
Carbon	0.15–0.45
Manganese	0.50–1.00
Silicon	0.20–0.75
Sulphur	0.06 max.
Phosphorus	0.05 max.

Steel castings are made in accordance with A.S.T.M. Specification A27–24, which covers two types of castings:

Class A: castings for which no physical requirements are specified.

Class B: castings for which physical requirements are specified. There are three grades: hard, medium, and soft, which indicate certain limiting physical properties.

The 0.25 per cent carbon steel casting, commonly used for machine-base construction, has a good combination of ductility and strength. There is very little difference in physical properties between this metal and hot-rolled boiler plate or machinery steel.

It is more difficult to make a good grade of cast steel than a similar grade of cast iron because of the higher pouring temperature and the greater shrinkage that the steel undergoes, which cause high internal stresses. Cast steel is subject to the dangers of blowholes, slag inclusions, segregation, and an undesirable grain structure.

Any casting that is welded should preferably have a carbon content not exceeding 0.30 per cent. It should be stress-relieved or annealed to remove all strains and to avoid serious cracking that may result from the local application of heat.

Alloy-Steel Castings

Alloy additions to cast steel are made to improve the strength, resistance to impact, abrasive resistance, and strength at high temperatures. The most generally used alloys are nickel-chromium, molybdenum, vanadium, and manganese, which may be used singly or in combination. Table 2–2 shows the physical properties of the more common cast alloy steels.

(1) *Nickel steel.* Nickel increases the tensile strength without sacrificing the ductility. Castings of nickel steel are selected for rugged use when high strength and resistance to fatigue and impact are the chief requirements, as in rolling-mill machinery.

(2) *Chromium steel.* Chromium forms carbides, increases the hardenability of the steel, and is particularly useful in increasing the strength and wear resistance. This alloy is used for machinery parts such as sprockets and sheaves which are subject to considerable abrasion. The usual analysis is as follows:

> Chromium 0.50–0.90%
> Carbon 0.35–0.45%

(3) *Chromium-nickel steel.* This alloy, S.A.E. 3140, is also used for wear resistance. Molybdenum is frequently added to impart better machining qualities.

(4) *Manganese-molybdenum steel.* This alloy is particularly well suited for service requiring a high resistance to wear and shock, and general toughness.

(5) *Vanadium steel.* Vanadium steel is often used in machinery frames when high resistance to impact and fatigue are paramount.

Nonferrous Castings

Nonferrous castings are widely used in the machinery field for bearings, cams, valves, and gears. Though they are important machine parts, they have little use in the machine frame itself.

TABLE 2-2

PROPERTIES OF ALLOY-STEEL CASTINGS

Composition	Tensile strength, lb. per sq. in.	Yield point, lb. per sq. in.	Elongation in 2 in., %	Reduction in area, %	Weight, lb. per cu. ft.
Ni 2.00–2.25 C 0.20–0.30 Mn 0.80–1.00 Si 0.25–0.40 Ph 0.05 max. Heat-treated	90,000 to 105,000	55,000 to 65,000	22 to 28	42 to 55	480
Cr 0.50–0.90 C 0.35–0.45 Heat-treated	97,000	55,000	19	30	480
Mn 1.00 C 0.35 Mo 0.40 Heat-treated	96,000	68,000	26	58	430
Va 0.16–0.20 C 0.30–0.40 Mn 0.80–1.00 Heat-treated	95,000	65,000	18	30	480
Cr 18.00 Ni 8.00 Si 2.00 Mn 1.00 C 0.15	70,000	30,000	35	40	480
Cr 11.5–13.5 Ni 0.80 Si 1.00 Mn 0.75 C 0.15	85,000	55,000	20	40	480

Nonferrous Alloy Castings of Low Specific Gravity

The aluminum and magnesium alloys are very light in comparison to steel and must be considered in machine design when extremely low weight is the principal consideration. Three of the most important light sand-cast alloys, with their salient physical properties, are listed in Table 2–3.

TABLE 2–3

SAND-CAST ALLOYS OF LOW SPECIFIC GRAVITY

Property	$\left(\begin{matrix}\text{Al} & 92\% \\ \text{Cu} & 8\%\end{matrix}\right)$	$\left(\begin{matrix}\text{Al} & 95\% \\ \text{Si} & 5\%\end{matrix}\right)$	Dowmetal: $\left(\begin{matrix}\text{Mg} & 91\% \\ \text{Al} & 6\% \\ \text{Mn} & 0.2\% \\ \text{Zn} & 3\%\end{matrix}\right)$
Tensile strength, p.s.i.	20,000	20,000	27,000
Yield point, p.s.i.	14,000	12,000	12,000
Elongation in 2 in., %	1.5	4.5	6.0
Modulus of elasticity	10,300,000	10,300,000	. . . . . .
Brinell hardness	60	43	49
Weight, lb. per cu. ft.	180	168	113

Low-Carbon Hot-rolled Steel

Welded machine bases are generally fabricated from ordinary hot-rolled steel that conforms to S.A.E. 1020 specifications or to A.S.T.M. specifications A7–42 and A10–34 for standard structural plates, shapes, and bars. The S.A.E. steel analysis is as follows:

COMPOSITION OF S.A.E. 1020 STEEL

Metal	*Per Cent*
Carbon...................	0.15–0.25
Manganese................	0.30–0.60
Phosphorus...............	0.45 max.
Sulphur..................	0.045 max.

Boiler plate and machinery and warehouse steel all conform to this specification, which is generally available in a wide variety of shapes and sizes. It has very little tendency to harden when flame-cut or welded and is sufficiently ductile to be bent or formed within reasonable limits without material injury to its physical properties. Consequently, it is ideal for fabrication work. Low-carbon hot-rolled steel is, for all practical purposes, dense, homogeneous, and uniform in physical properties. The metal is free from brittleness and has a high resistance to shock and fatigue stresses. The tensile strength and ductility are both excellent. The modulus of elasticity is high, and the compressive strength is about equal to the tensile strength. The material corrodes readily unless protected by paint, and it scales rapidly at high temperatures. It is dense and oiltight, even down to the lightest gauge.

Steel has elastic properties which are definitely superior to those of ordinary cast iron. The stress-strain curve of ordinary cast iron is not linear; that is, the proportionality between the stress and the corresponding deformation or strain, even at relatively low stresses, does not follow a straight line. Consequently, the deformation produced in any element of cast iron is partly elastic and partly plastic, thereby resulting in a permanent set. In steel, the stress-strain relation is represented by a straight line up to the elastic limit beyond which a slight increase in stress will produce a considerable increase in strain.

Cast iron will damp out vibrations more rapidly than steel, but for resisting vibration stresses steel is superior because of its higher elastic limit and resistance to fatigue.

In a welded steel structure, there is distortion only when stresses exceed the elastic limit. The designer has only to make certain that the working stress plus the residual stresses is below the elastic limit in the final structure. For this reason, it is important to specify stress-relieving to nullify any residual stresses in a base that is to be highly stressed in service.

Low-Alloy High-Strength Steels

The use of low-alloy high-strength steel is expected to increase considerably, since such steels are superior to the plain low-carbon steels in tensile strength, yield point, and fatigue and impact resistance. They have two to three times the abrasive resistance of low-carbon steel and more than twice the resistance to atmospheric corrosion. Also, they have high ductility and great density. The forming and cutting characteristics of these alloy steels are good and they are readily weldable. In welding, an electrode similar in analysis to the plate should be used. Most of these steels show very little air-hardening tendencies adjacent to the welded seam, a desirable quality in structures that are subjected to impact and fatigue stresses.

In design, it is important to remember that the modulus of elasticity of all steels is approximately the same. When deflection is the chief requirement, the higher strengths of the low-alloy high-strength steels are of little importance, unless it is possible to re-distribute the metal in such a way as to make up in stiffness for the loss resulting from weight reduction. When tensile strength is the important factor, it is possible to use a higher unit stress in design and reduce the weight of the member considerably.

Metals and Special Alloys Available for Fabrication

Some special metals and alloys available in the form of rolled plate and other shapes are listed below. All these materials may be fabricated by welding. The cost of most of them prohibits their general use in heavy machine-base construction, although some are used in the fabrication of bases for small machine units. Others have special characteristics that should be considered for unusual applications.[2]

FERROUS METALS

Ingot iron: Almost pure iron. (Carbon content is 0.01 to 0.05 per cent. All elements other than iron total less than 0.16 per cent.) Good corrosion resistance. Available in sheets and plates.

S.A.E. 2315: $3\frac{1}{2}$ per cent nickel steel, for high strength and toughness, and high strength at low temperatures.

Stainless steels: The 18 per cent chrome—8 per cent nickel, and the 25 per cent chrome—12 per cent nickel alloys are easily fabricated and used for corrosion resistance. Good work-hardening properties, toughness, heat resistance, machinability.

High-manganese steel: 12 to 14 per cent manganese, 0.5 to 1.25 per cent carbon, 3 to 5 per cent nickel. High resistance to shock abrasion.

Copper bearing steel: 0.20–0.50 per cent copper content gives increased rust resistance.

---

[2] For additional information, the designer is referred to the *Metals Handbook*, American Society for Metals, Cleveland, 1939.

NONFERROUS METALS

Copper: For welded fabrication, the metal should be deoxidized. Should contain a small amount of silicon or phosphorus.

Brass and bronze: Available in many analyses. Generally used in chemical installations because of corrosion-resisting properties.

Aluminum (Pure and Alloyed): Widely used where extremely low specific gravity is essential. Available in special rolled shapes.

Magnesium: Dowmetal available in sheets, strips, and extruded shapes. For applications requiring extremely low specific gravity.

Monel metal: Nickel-copper alloy, for corrosion resistance.

CHAPTER 3

Stress-Analysis and Design Data

THE OBJECT of machine design is to create a structure that will be capable of performing the required tasks and at the same time be economical to fabricate. The best design, therefore, will be one that will do the required work with the least total cost per unit. The designer must be familiar with all methods of fabrication in order to be able to pick the most favorable method. In addition, he must be thoroughly versed in all methods of stress analysis, because changing from one method of fabrication to another often changes stress distributions, and a new analysis must be made. For the many structures that are statically indeterminate or too complicated for a complete stress analysis, the designer must rely on his experience and judgment.

In the design of any weldment, the fundamental formulas of tension, compression, shear, bending, and deflection are applicable when used with the proper working stresses. However, the many intricate parts and connections that may easily be made by welding have complicated the design problem by the introduction of eccentric loads and secondary stresses, which the designer must constantly keep in mind.

Special Considerations

In many machines, especially heavy bases, the primary consideration is rigidity rather than strength. In the past these parts have been made of cast iron, but now many are being made by welding together standard steel sections and plates. Theoretically, a steel structure of the same cross section as a cast-iron structure will deflect only half as much as the one made of cast iron, since the modulus of elasticity of steel is 30,000,000 p.s.i. as compared to 15,000,000 p.s.i. for ordinary gray cast iron. Therefore, it would seem logical to say that a steel part with half the area of a cast-iron part would be as rigid as the cast iron. However, since the rigidity of a part is dependent on the moment of inertia of the cross section as well as the modulus of elasticity, it is necessary to think in terms of the moment of inertia and not the area. For example, if a bar of steel and a bar of cast iron each 2 in. square and of the same length are supported at the ends and loaded at the center with the same load, the cast-iron bar will deflect twice as much as the steel bar. If the steel bar is made 1 in. wide and 2 in. deep, the two bars will deflect the same amount, since the moment of inertia of the steel bar is one-half the moment of inertia of the cast-iron bar. If the steel bar is made 2 in. wide and 1 in. deep, it will deflect four times as much as the cast-iron bar, since its moment of inertia is now only one-eighth that of the cast-iron bar, although its area is one-half that of the cast-iron bar.

In considering a change from one material to another in any structure, other characteristics than strength must be considered. It is well known that cast iron is more efficient in damping out vibrations than steel but that steel is more resistant to shock than cast iron. Steel is more ductile than cast iron, and on this account is less susceptible to fatigue failure and is better able to resist stress concentrations.

Stress Analysis

Every large or complex weldment is a special problem in stress analysis, and no general rules covering every case can be laid down. Each problem must be studied and analyzed in accordance with the use to which the structure is to be put. The loads may be static or dynamic; if the latter, then fatigue and possibly impact conditions must be considered. Certain sections, under compression, may be long enough so that they must be considered as columns; others, in tension, may be so short that they may behave as brittle materials because of the lack of length in which to deform.

A detailed design of a weldment would be of little value here, since it would naturally be a specialized problem of direct interest to only a few readers. However, it is advisable to review some of the fundamental formulas for stress.

Fundamental Equations

In direct axial tension or compression on short members, the stress is assumed to be uniformly distributed over the cross-sectional area and is given by the equation

$$S = \frac{P}{A},$$

where the area A is at right angles to the axis of the member. This equation also assumes that the member is uniform in cross section throughout its length with no discontinuities to cause stress concentrations. Stress concentrations are set up at points where there is an abrupt change in cross section or an obstacle to the free flow of stress from one section to another. As an example, suppose a 2-in. plate is butt-welded to a 6-in. plate and that the section is subjected to a tensile load. The stresses at the edges of the 2-in. plate at the joint may be from two to two and a half times the stress in the plate at some distance from the weld.

In shear, the equation for the direct stress is also $S = P/A$, but here the area is parallel to the load and the stress is caused by two equal and opposite parallel loads.

For bending, the equation

$$S = \frac{MC}{I}$$

gives the stress for any bending moment M and for any fiber at a distance C from the neutral axis. For maximum stress, the moment M is the maximum moment set up by the external loads, C is the distance from the neutral axis to the fiber farthest from the neutral axis, and I is the moment of inertia of the cross-sectional area about the neutral axis.

In many machines and machine parts, deformations and deflections are of primary importance. For direct tension or compression, the total deformation is given by the equation

$$d = \frac{PL}{AE},$$

where L is the length over which the deformation is measured. In bending, there is no single equation that will give the deflection, since the deflection is dependent on the position of the loads and the method of support as well as the modulus of elasticity, length of the beam, and the moment of inertia. As an example, for a simple beam supported at the ends and carrying a single concentrated load P at the center, the maximum deflection is at the center and is given by the equation

$$d = \frac{PL^3}{48EI},$$

where L is the distance between supports, E is the modulus of elasticity, and I is the moment of inertia of the cross-sectional area. Table A, Appendix I, gives several examples of deflection equations for various types of beams and loadings.

Loads on symmetrical tension or short compression members that are not applied along the geometrical axis of the member but have an eccentricity e will set up a combined stress condition which requires the use of an equation involving the direct stress P/A and a bending stress Pec/I. For instance, suppose a short section of I-beam is welded to a plate and an eccentric load is applied to the end of the I-beam, as in Fig. 3–1. The weld at A would be subjected to a direct compressive stress of P/A and a tensile stress caused by bending of Pec/I. Thus the resulting stress at A would be

$$S = \frac{P}{A} - \frac{Pec}{I};$$

at B the bending stress would be compressive, so the resulting stress would be

$$S = \frac{P}{A} + \frac{Pec}{I}.$$

If the I-beam is in contact with the plate over its entire cross section, A in the first term should be taken as the area of the I-beam plus the area of the weld (hl) on each side. If the I-beam is not in contact with the plate, then A is the area of the welds only. The term Pec/I in both cases would be given by the expression $1.414Pe/hl(b + h)$.

Another case of unsymmetrical loading would be where an angle or channel is welded to a plate and a tensile or compressive load is applied along the neutral axis of the member. In this case, if l_1 and l_2 (Fig. 3–2) are made the same length, a couple would be set up that would introduce a second stress in addition to the direct

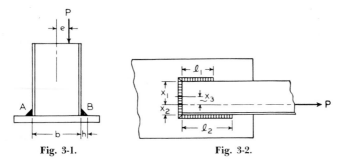

Fig. 3-1.   **Fig. 3-2.**

stress. To avoid this condition, the joint is designed so that the strength of the welds will balance each other; that is,

$$S_1 l_1 x_1 = S_2 l_2 x_2$$

where S_1 and S_2 are the strengths of the welds in pounds per inch (generally taken as $10{,}000h$ for shielded arc welds). If there is a transverse weld, it must be included in the equation; thus

$$S_1 l_1 x_1 + S_3 (x_1 + x_2) x_3 = S_2 l_2 x_2$$

where S_3 is the strength per inch of length of the transverse weld.

Combined stresses also occur in transverse fillet-welded joints subjected to bending, as illustrated in Figs. 3–3 and 3–4.

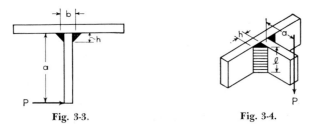

Fig. 3-3.   **Fig. 3-4.**

In Fig. 3–3 the stresses in the welds are found by assuming first that the bending moment Pa is resisted by a couple composed of forces acting at the center of the fusion zones of the welds:

$$S_1 = \frac{Pa}{0.707 h b l} = \frac{1.414 Pa}{b h l}.$$

In addition to this stress there is a direct shearing stress on the welds:

$$S_2 = \frac{P/2}{0.707hl} = \frac{0.707P}{hl}.$$

The resulting combined shearing stress is then given by the equation

$$S_s = \sqrt{S_1^2 + S_2^2}$$

or

$$S_s = \frac{P}{hlb}\sqrt{\frac{4a^2 + b^2}{2}}$$

In Fig. 3–4 the weld is subjected to a bending stress of

$$S_1 = \frac{6Pa}{0.707h2l_2}$$

and a direct shear stress of

$$S_2 = \frac{P}{0.707h2l},$$

and the resulting combined shearing stress is given by the equation

$$S_s = \sqrt{\frac{S_2^2 + S_1^2}{4}}$$

or

$$S_s = \frac{0.707P}{hl^2}\sqrt{l^2 + 9a^2}$$

In all the foregoing equations the minimum shear area is through the center of the fillet and is equal to $h \cos 45$ deg. or $0.707hl$.

Additional equations for various stress conditions are given in Appendix I-D.

Special Welds

Some consideration should be given to special conditions which are not covered by ordinary equations but for which ordinary commercial practice is the governing factor.

For intermittent welds the recommended practice is to make the center to center spacing between increments 16 times the thickness of the thinner member in compression and 32 times the thickness of the thinner member for other loadings. In no case should the spacing be greater than 12 in. between adjacent welds.

Bearing pads and other parts that require subsequent machining should have the welds designed strong enough to withstand the machining forces, which may be larger than the actual service loads. Pads that have a width over 12 times their thickness should be plug-welded at the center to prevent the center from bulging. The plugs should be from two to four times the thickness of the plate.

Working Stresses

In the design of any welded joint it is important to know what working stresses can be used. Many tests have been made on both butt and fillet welds subjected to tension, compression, bending, and fatigue. From these tests working stresses for most conditions of loading have been deduced and codified (see Appendix I, Tables C through K).

The strength of most welds varies depending upon the design of the joint and the type of loading. Stress concentrations may be present that will increase the normal stress from two to three times its apparent value. Combinations of stresses are nearly always present, causing a resultant stress higher than the direct stresses. All these factors must be kept in mind when working stresses are applied to any given problems.

Inspection and Testing

Inspection of welded parts is usually simple. Such defects as sand holes, cold shuts, and porosity usually associated with the casting process are not a factor in the inspection of welded steel. The only point at which any inspection is necessary at all is where the homogeneous steel plates have been fused by the arc-welding process. And then the inspection is usually limited to visual observation of the weld bead itself, to determine whether it conforms to the adopted standard of size and shape. Since the weld metal is always stronger than the parent mild steel, small imperfections are of little consequence in the ability of the weld to resist normal stresses. There are certain applications such as high-pressure vessels and parts such as turbine blades, propellers, which are exposed to high impact and fatigue loads and therefore demand rigid inspection such as the use of X-ray, magna-flux or Zyglo. Summarizing, we may say that visual inspection is adequate for almost all weldments other than those in which the welded joint is subjected to high fatigue or impact loads and for those applications in which inspection is controlled by codes and specifications such as are adopted by the American Welding Society and the American Society for Testing Materials.

CHAPTER 4

Designing Arc-Welded Machine Bases

IN MANY of the early attempts to fabricate machine-tool bases, the casting design was copied without any thought of a simplified redesign. In following this procedure the designer overlooked the fact that many elements of the cast design are present merely because of the nature of the casting process. The casting designer thinks in terms of metal flow and shrinkage, the pattern and the core and how they function, and finally in terms of the foundry and the mechanics of the casting process. Consequently, cast designs are characterized by their general massiveness, long curves, tapered sides, and sweeping fillets. Ribs are frequently incorporated for the sole purpose of facilitating pouring and to counteract cooling strains. It is also the general practice to try to equalize the thickness of all ribs, partitions, and wall sections in order to obtain uniform cooling rates and hardness throughout the casting. It is readily apparent that if a welding design merely copies a cast design, it will often be inefficient.

Good welding design takes into account all the inherent advantages of the arc-welding process and of the metal being fabricated. The designer of welded construction should consider both fabrication and cost requirements. All functional requirements should be met with a design of minimum weight. The design should be simple, with bending supplanting welding as much as feasible. The amount of welding should be ample but not excessive, and should be specified. Rolled sections should be incorporated into the design wherever possible. The minimum number of parts should be used. In quantity production the design should be adapted for automatic welding if possible, in order to minimize fabrication costs.

Flexibility in Design

The foremost advantage of arc-welded construction is the extreme flexibility of the process. This feature accounts for welded designs which are impossible by other methods. An oil pan of light-gauge metal may be made integral with a heavy machine frame, and a pressure reservoir may be incorporated within a base. As a result of this flexibility, the welded machine-base designer has created a new design, the enclosed box section, which is the most efficient structure so far developed by any method for resisting complicated stresses in a machine base. The enclosed box section is excellent in resisting tension, compression, bending, and torsion, and it develops maximum rigidity with minimum weight and at correspondingly low cost.

The flexibility of arc-welded construction permits alteration of the machine base structure either in the course of its construction or after it is completed, since it is a simple matter to alter welded construction by adding or subtracting material. On new experimental types of machines, changes in the design that cannot be anticipated before fabrication starts are sometimes necessary. A welded base may be placed in service and found to be deficient in stiffness. An additional stiffening rib may be added where it is needed. A boss may require relocation. The old boss is removed with the oxyacetylene cutting torch and a new one is quickly welded in its proper location. Alterations of this type are of little consequence if accomplished before the base is stress-relieved and finish-machined. After stress relief and machining, a careful check should be made to determine if the additional application of heat has resulted in distortion. Minor changes may be made without appreciable change in the structure, but major alterations may distort the base to such an extent as to require a new stress-relief treatment followed by a remachining operation.

Weight Reduction and Welding Design

Any design requirement that emphasizes minimum weight favors welded steel. The most important physical property of a material for machine-base construction is a high modulus of elasticity, that is, a high resistance to deformation. The designer takes the modulus of elasticity as the measure of rigidity. For example, steel is more rigid than ordinary cast iron in the ratio of 30,000,000 to

12,000,000; and in respect to the stronger grades of alloy cast iron, the ratio is about 30,000,000 to 22,000,000. According to these ratios the weight of the welded steel base can be reduced about 50 per cent with respect to ordinary cast iron and 25 per cent with respect to alloy cast iron and develop the same rigidity, everything being similar. Reductions of this magnitude are not always possible because of the factor of distribution. Rigidity depends not only on how much metal is present but also on how it is arranged or distributed. A long base of box construction is very flimsy if no cross-bracing ribs are present even though the weight of the steel is ample. The designer makes use of ribs and cold forming to develop the necessary stiffness in a weldment. If full use is made of weight reductions and ample ribbing is provided, the steel design should be lighter than the cast iron design by 40 to 15 per cent, respectively.

No similar reduction in weight is possible with respect to cast steel because it has the same modulus of elasticity as rolled steel. However, welded designs in general should be considerably lighter than either cast-iron or cast-steel designs created for similar purposes merely by the elimination of elements essential to the casting process but nonessential to the welding process. As has been previously mentioned, a lighter-weight design also results from the welding designer's ability to use the lightest materials necessary to satisfy physical requirements alone, whereas the cast design must satisfy both foundry and physical requirements. For example, oil pans and oil reservoirs may be fabricated out of light rolled-steel plate, which is oiltight down to the lightest gauges, whereas it is impractical to go much below ⅜ in. in cast designs because of the possibility of oil seepage and also because of casting limitations.

Elimination of Machining Operations

Some of the greatest economies in welded construction result from the elimination of machining operations. As a concrete illustration, many machine bases have oiltight access doors. The surface of a casting is rough, and wherever such an oiltight cover is required it is customary to cast a ridge around the opening. This ridge is later machined and the cover plate is bolted in place with an oiltight gasket. Welding designers eliminate the ridge and the machining operation because the hot-rolled plate is flat and smooth.

A hole is cut for the door and the cover plate is bolted directly to the plate with a gasket. If greater thread depth is required for the bolts than is afforded by the thickness of the side wall, a frame is flame-cut and welded around the opening.

Important pads and bosses on large bases can be accurately located after the machine-base frame has been fabricated and checked for straightness. In this way it is possible to minimize the amount of material that must be removed in finishing operations.

Uniformity of Rolled Steel

Rolled plate is uniform in thickness within narrow limits. Any rolled shape such as a channel or I-beam is also uniform throughout its length within narrow limits. A machine base that has side plates of a given thickness will accordingly have a wall structure on all sides of uniform thickness within narrow mill limits. The thickness variations are so slight that it is unnecessary to make allowances in the design. On the other hand, cast designs with complicated coring may have considerable inequality in opposite wall thicknesses due to core shifting in pouring operations. In such cases it may be necessary to make allowance in the design, particularly when machining operations are necessary.

Resonance

The natural frequency should be as high as possible for high-speed machines in order to avoid the possibility of resonance. The weight of a machine bed is an important factor in regard to vibrations caused by resonance. For a given structure the natural frequency is inversely proportional to the square root of the weight. The natural frequency then increases as the weight decreases. Welded construction is favorable to a high frequency because of its relatively low weight.

The welded machine base should be designed in such a manner as to avoid a wide expanse in an unsupported plate. Such an unsupported plate can readily act as a drum and respond to the vibrations set up in the machine. Three devices are used to break up vibrations in welded designs: holes, ribs and stiffeners, and dissimilar metals with different physical properties. The main object in each of these methods is to disrupt the continuity of the structure and thereby prevent the transmission of vibrations.

Tension and Compression Loading

Rolled or cast steel is about equally resistant to both tension and compression stresses. In referring to steel, the casting and the rolled section are both included, since these materials have approximately the same physical properties when similar in composition. Ordinary cast iron is relatively weak in tension and considerably stronger than steel in compression. The designer of gray-iron castings generally favors compression loading. The draw cut is favored over the push cut for this reason. Alloy cast irons have tensile strengths approaching or equal to that of mild steel, and they also have a much higher compression strength.

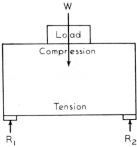

Fig. 4-1. Machine base under load.

Ordinary and alloy cast iron are both superior to steel in their capacity to resist pure compression loads. Many machine bases, however, are long enough to be considered as simple beams under load, and they are subject to flexural stresses. Bending involves tension as well as compression. The matter of deflection is the important consideration, and the designer is particularly concerned about the modulus of elasticity of the material and the moment of inertia of the section (Fig. 4-1).

Practical Design

It is the purpose here to approach the problem of welding design from the practical standpoint as the fabricator analyzes it. The fabricator and the designer working in close harmony on many different types of machine frames have evolved certain design principles that promote economy as well as beauty of line.

The simplest and the most commonly used type of box design is shown in Fig. 4-2.

The bottom rail (1) supports the base. The designer should consult a warehouse stock list and select a standard bar size for his layout; otherwise the fabricator will find it necessary to flame-cut the bar from plate at a considerable increase in cost. The designer should also examine the stock list to see if the section which he proposes to use carries an extra charge. If it does, it is quite possible that he can substitute a size that carries no extra charge. The corners of the bottom rail are shown rounded. It is good practice to make all the welds in the bottom bars vee butt welds and to grind off all reinforcement. The fabricator usually allows ¼ in. extra

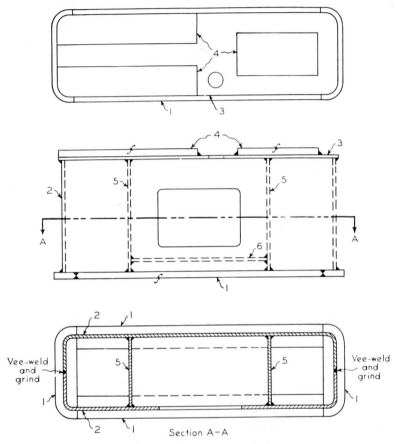

Fig. 4-2. Box-type construction with rounded corners.

material for a machined surface, so he uses a bar ¼ in. thicker than the drawing indicates. Some designers make their own allowances for machine work and incorporate these dimensions on their work without any finish marks. If they allow ample material, all is well, but considerable trouble ensues if scanty allowance is made. The best practice is to show the finished dimension and leave the matter of extra metal to the fabricator, who will take into account the size of the weldment and the problems involved in maintaining straightness.

The side wall (2) is made of two U-shaped pieces which are vee-welded. All weld reinforcement is removed by grinding, so that when the base is painted there is no indication of any weld in the side walls. Round corners with a fairly large radius are easily prepared in the brake, and they give a pleasing appearance to the base.

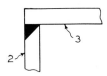

Item 3 is a top cover plate. Item 2 is shown fillet-welded to items 1 and 3. The fillet weld is the least expensive type and makes a good appearance. The top cover plate (3) may be flush with the side plate (2) and vee-welded as shown

Fig. 4-3. Top cover plate flush with side plate.

by Fig. 4–3, but this construction is more costly, since the plate must first be vee'd and then the weld reinforcement must be ground off. The outside fillet welds (both top and bottom) are made continuous for good appearance irrespective of the question of oiltightness. The three bedplates (4) are united to the cover plate by continuous fillet welds for oiltightness.

Ribs (5) are added to stiffen the base in support of the bedplates. Plate 6 is added to give a bottom to a special oil chamber located between ribs (5). All ribs 5 and 6 should be double-welded to assure oiltightness. The fabricator uses two light fillets instead of one heavy bead because occasionally a single fillet will leak oil at a crater or overlapping point. The designer should specify oiltightness where it is required.

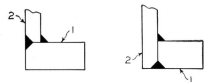

Fig. 4-4. Alternate methods for attaching side plate (2) to bottom rail (1).

Alternative methods for attaching side plates (2) to the bottom rail (1) are shown in Fig. 4–4.

Oil catches are sometimes built around the top cover plate. The coolant or lubricant is returned in this manner to the oil sump. Three common types of oil catches are shown in Fig. 4–5.

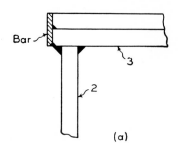

(a)

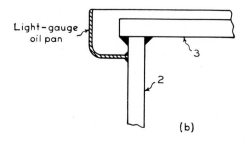

(b)

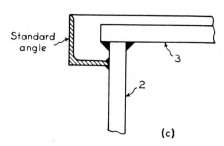

(c)

Fig. 4-5. Oil catches.

Machine bases with side plates having a pronounced flare or skirt at the bottom are shown in Fig. 4–6 (a, b). Two types of flare are shown. These are formed in a press brake. At the corners the design requires a curvature in two directions. It is customary to make special corner sections by hot-forging in a special die. Another method is to use steel castings. Some commercial welderies have standardized these corner pieces and keep a stock on hand. If the corner piece is prepared by hot-forging, it may be made of lighter

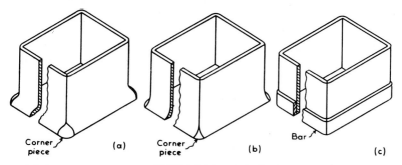

Fig. 4-6. (a, b) Flared bases. (c) Bar stiffener for base.

material than the body of the base. The lighter metal forms more easily than a heavier piece, and it will fill in the corner just as well and will cost less to weld in place.

Fig. 4–6 (c) shows a bar welded to the bottom of the side plates, to stiffen it. This bar is easily formed and looks good.

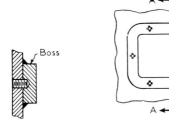

Fig. 4-7. Boss to back up drilling for greater thread depth.

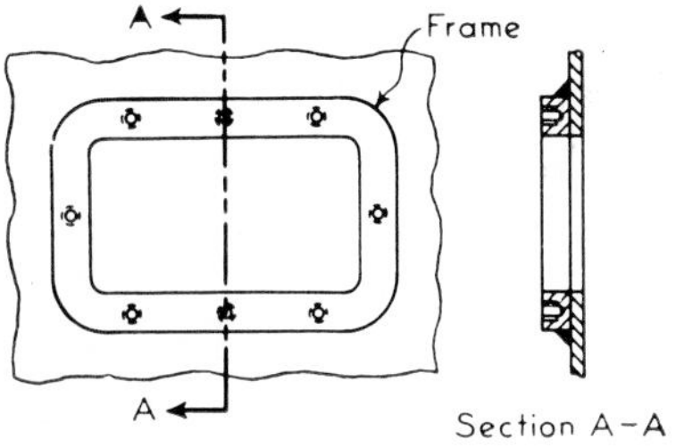

Fig. 4-8. Frame for a cutout.

Where the side-wall thickness is insufficient for drilling and tapping for bolts to attach a cover plate, as is frequently the case, it is customary to back up the hole with a boss to give greater depth to the threads (Fig. 4–7). Another method for increasing the depth of threads is shown in Fig. 4–8.

In a heavy weldment some provision is usually made for lifting or shifting the position of the base. A common design for a lifting lug is shown in Fig. 4–9.

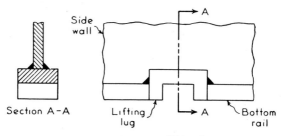

Fig. 4-9. Design for a lifting lug.

Lugs are welded to the bottom-rail section for tie-down bolts (Figs. 4–10 and 4–11).

Figure 4–12 shows a number of bracket designs.

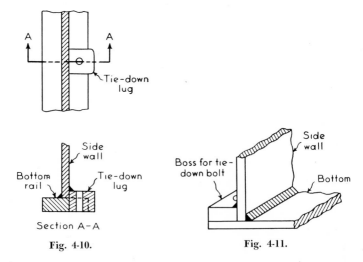

Fig. 4-10.

Fig. 4-11.

A method for tying down a machine bed with anchor bolts is shown in Fig. 4–13.

Heavy plate, 3/4 in. and greater in thickness, exceeding the press-brake capacity for bending the particular lengths in question, may be fabricated with nicely rounded corners as shown in Fig. 4–14. The outside corner welds are made full and then ground to a

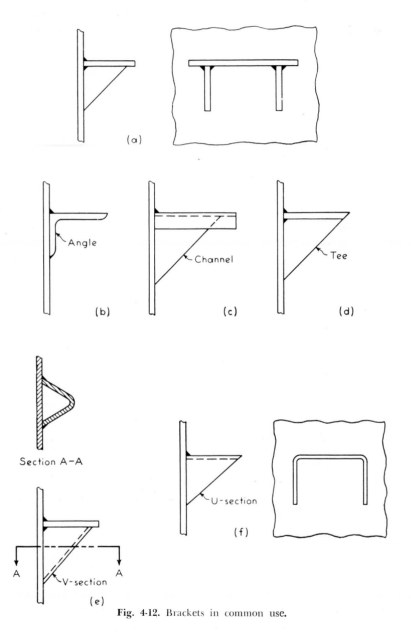

Fig. 4-12. Brackets in common use.

uniform radius. The inside should be fillet-welded for added
strength.

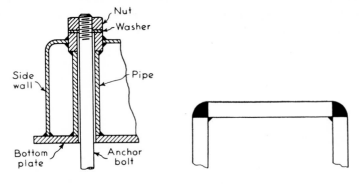

Fig. 4-13. Anchor bolt
attachment.

Fig. 4-14. Heavy plate, corner-
welded.

Figure 4–15 shows a section of a Diesel-engine bed. The high
side walls add greatly to the stiffness of the base, permitting the use
of rather light plate for the side walls and ribs.

Figure 4–16 shows a one-piece door chute of common design.

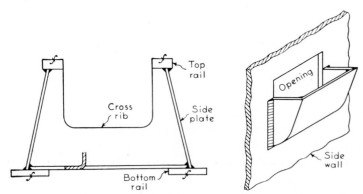

Fig. 4-15. Diesel-engine bed.

Fig. 4-16. One-piece door
chute.

Hot-rolled steel shapes are frequently used in fabricating low-
type bases of rather large area. In weldment construction in general, it is economical to use rolled sections because they provide the
maximum stiffness with the least amount of labor. For example, a

certain beam section costs under 4 cents a pound. Fabricating the same section out of plate material would cost perhaps 12 to 15 cents a pound. By incorporating such sections in weldment designs where the shapes can be used for promoting stiffness, the cost is lowered appreciably. Large bases of the low type made up largely of H-beams or channels for the framework and including cover plates, oil compartments, and bedplates and bosses have been built for 30 to 50 per cent less than corresponding all-plate construction. Figure 4–17 shows a frame of this type consisting of wide-flange H-beams.

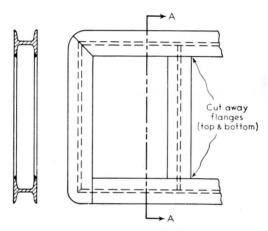

Fig. 4-17. Low base with wide-flange beams.

Figure 4–18 shows the different types of hot-rolled steel sections that are generally available through mill and warehouse sources. The common ranges in sizes with corresponding weights are also listed. The steel mills are always interested in rolling any new section for which there is a sufficient demand. As the use of welding is extended it seems likely that new sections will appear to simplify the process of fabrication.

The principles involved in automotive design may be used to advantage in machine-base design. The automobile has a heavy rugged frame which supports the load. The frame is covered with a light-gauge sheet of attractive design. The manufacturer varies this design from year to year to attract the fancy of the buyer, but the interior framework remains pretty much the same for several years. In a similar manner a machine base may be constructed out of heavy rolled sections and this frame may be covered with light-gauge sheet metal to give a streamlined effect (Fig. 4–19).

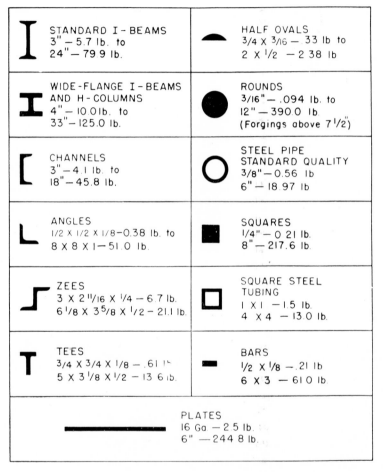

Fig. 4-18. Common sizes for hot-rolled sections.

Figure 4–20 shows a frame constructed of channels. At the corners the flanges are slotted and the web is bent to give a rounded corner. The joints are welded inside for the H-beam and channel frames.

Figure 4–21 shows a lifting hook built into a channel section.

This same type of hook is also attached to I-beams and to the side plates of a weldment of purely plate construction.

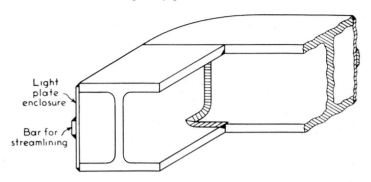

Light plate enclosure

Bar for streamlining

Fig. 4-19. H-column base.

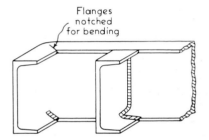

Flanges notched for bending

Fig. 4-20. Channel base.

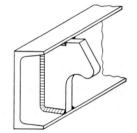

Fig. 4-21. Lifting hook attached to channel.

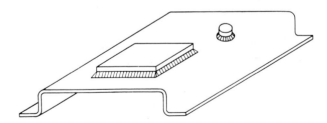

Fig. 4-22. Electric-motor base.

A common type of motor-base design is shown in Fig. 4–22. The body of the base is formed out of a single plate in a press brake. Figure 4–23 shows five different methods of fabricating beam sections.

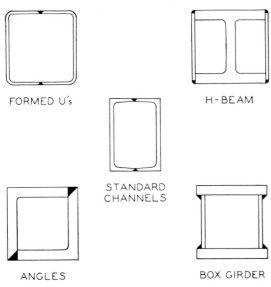

FORMED U's

H-BEAM

STANDARD CHANNELS

ANGLES

BOX GIRDER

Fig. 4-23. Fabricated beam sections.

Figure 4–24 shows a box-type frame constructed entirely of angles of similar size. This type of construction is simple, economical, and very rigid. In order to clarify the frame construction, all attachments have been omitted. The designer may add four base plates at the bottom, to be machined along the bottom surface. A light cover plate may be added at the top with lugs or bosses welded in place. If an oil sump is required, the designer can add a ¼-in. plate inside at the bottom. The spaces between the four vertical posts may be taken up by light plate covers and a louver door.

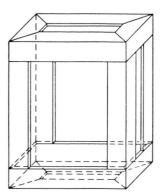

Fig. 4-24. Frame constructed of similar-size angles.

As previously stated, the designer should strive at all times to use rolled sections or bent plate in order to minimize the amount of welding. An example of good welding design is illustrated in Fig. 4–25. A single plate burned to template is formed in a press brake along the dotted lines to produce a sturdy workbench. A certain type of machine bed could be developed in similar fashion. The only welding required is to join the four corners, which are notched. If quantity lots are required, the plates may be stack-burned at a considerable reduction in cost. If the quantity exceeds a thousand pieces it might be good economy to die-stamp the plate in a power press, though the thickness of the plate and the over-all size would have bearing on the choice of methods.

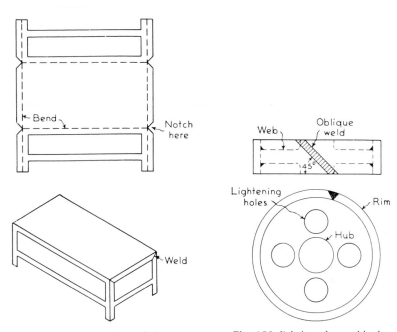

Fig. 4-25. Good welding design.   Fig. 4-26. Fabricated gear blank.

Figure 4–26 shows a large fabricated gear blank. The outer rim is S.A.E. 1045 steel, and the web and hub are S.A.E. 1020 steel. Holes are burned in the web to reduce the weight. The rim is vee butt-welded at an angle of 45 deg. so that the tooth outline cuts obliquely across the weld zone, to ensure that any slight difference in the hardness of the weld metal and the rim metal will not result in unequal tooth wear. The use of S.A.E. 1045 steel in the rim gives a tooth material which can be machined easily and which responds readily to flame-hardening to give excellent wearing qualities. The hub and web are made of S.A.E. 1020 steel, which gives greater ductility where it is needed. Fabricated gear blanks should always be stress-relieved before they are machined.

The fabricated gear blank illustrates another important advantage in the process of welding metals. In arc welding, the designer

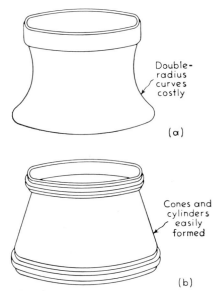

Double-
radius
curves
costly

(a)

Cones and
cylinders
easily
formed

(b)

Fig. 4-27. Base redesigned to simplify construction.

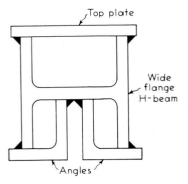

Top plate

Wide
flange
H-beam

Angles

Fig. 4-28. Design for a rigid bed.

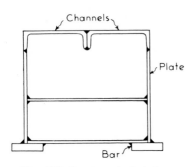

Channels

Plate

Bar

Fig. 4-29. Box-type bed design.

has his choice of metals to use at particular points to develop particular characteristics, whereas other processes of forming metals are limited to a single metal.

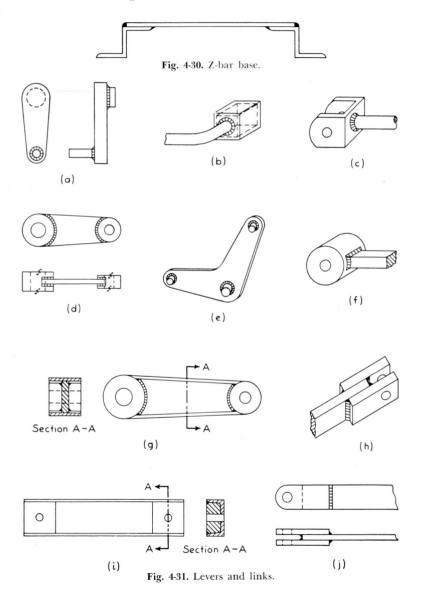

Fig. 4-30. Z-bar base.

(a)

(b)

(c)

(d)

(e)

(f)

Section A-A

(g)

(h)

(i)   Section A-A

(j)

Fig. 4-31. Levers and links.

Figure 4–27(a) shows a base of circular contour. It is very difficult and costly to form a base of this type in a press brake. The
chief difficulty lies in shaping the double-radius bends in the surface

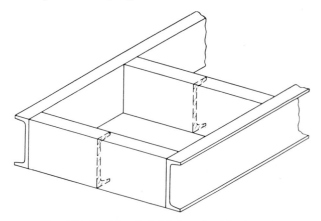

Fig. 4-32. Machine bed fabricated with channels.

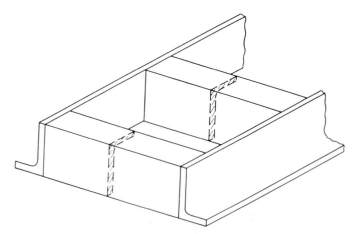

Fig. 4-33. Machine bed fabricated with angles.

of the base. A shape of this type in light-gauge metal could be made
very easily by spinning. The best procedure to follow in heavy plate
is the flanging and dishing process. The top and bottom sections
can be readily formed in this manner, and these sections can be
joined to a center cylindrical section. Figure 4–27(b) shows a close

approximation of the above base that may be readily formed in a press brake, since it is made up of cylinders and cones.

Figure 4–28 shows a design for a long bed of great rigidity. Rolled sections are used.

Figure 4–29 shows a box-type bed design in which channels and bars are used.

Figure 4–30 shows a motor base developed out of Z-bars and a plate.

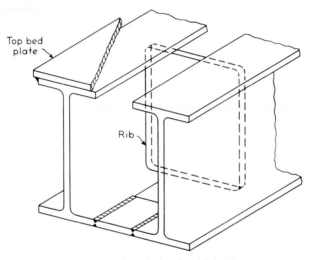

Fig. 4-34. Long box bed using high I-beams.

Figure 4–31 shows various types of levers and links of fabricated design.

Figures 4–32 and 4–33 show low-type machine beds in which, respectively, channels and angles are used. Such designs are simple and economical to fabricate.

Figure 4–34 shows the use of high I-beams in creating a long box bed of medium height. A bed of this type develops high rigidity and is economical to fabricate.

CHAPTER 5

Application of Welded-Design Principles

History

Since about 1930, when machine-base fabrication by welding began, many types have been built. The process has been applied to precision tools and to the frames of many highly stressed machine tools such as press brakes, punches, shears, and die-stamping units. There have also been many examples of fabricated beds, neither precision types nor highly stressed, designed merely to carry simple loads. Quantities have varied from one or a few of a kind for special machines to thousands of a kind for beds in continuous production. In the decade from 1938 to 1948, the authors observed possibly 500 different types of welded machine-base designs representing practically every field and phase of operation. In the course of this vast amount of work, many designs have been developed that should be of interest to the reader. Photographs of some of the outstanding types have been selected to illustrate the principles expressed in other chapters of this book.

Precision Machinery

One of the largest installations of fabricated precision machinery was made at the Industrial Rayon Corporation's plant at Painesville, Ohio (Fig. 5–1).

Figure 5–2, a close-up of the installation, shows the complete welded frame structure with transmission and front-drive enclosure. A total of 96 such machine frames, each comprising five panels on a side and totaling one mile in length, were fabricated and welded.

Production jig-welding methods effected remarkable savings on

COURTESY INDUSTRIAL RAYON CORP.

Fig. 5-1. Setting-up all-welded A-frames in a 3½ acre spinning room. At the extreme left are shown completed machines in operation. Toward their right are shown the A-frames in various phases of installation. Fabricated members for the machine frames appear in the foreground.

COURTESY INDUSTRIAL RAYON CORP.

Fig. 5-2. Assembling machine parts. This close-up of an installation in Fig. 5-1 shows the mounting of the power panel, including the double-output-shaft worm-gear drive for the inclined processing and drying section of the machine.

the structure. For example, preliminary designs embodying a good many castings, but with all the larger elements welded, showed a machining cost of $2750 per five-panel frame. By using jig welding, this machining cost was reduced to $175 per machine, and at the same time the cost was reduced on many machinery elements that were attached to the frame. The total weight of steel in this installation, including walks and floor structures, was approximately 3000 tons.

Fig. 5-3. A Summit-type dual-tire vulcanizing machine.

Box Construction

The base of a dual-tire vulcanizing machine (Fig. 5–3) illustrates the use of the welded box section and also the choice of weldments and steel castings on the basis of sound engineering and economy. The side links as well as the base are welded. The domes and their supporting arms are cast steel.

There are four bearing housings in the box-type bed. Two of these housings are built into the inside stiffeners, and the other two are welded into the outer walls. All are bored out for the shaft that connects the side links, which consist of heavy plate burned to size with bosses welded at the corners.

Highly Stressed Members

The press-brake frame is an excellent example of a machine base that not only supports the machine load but also is subject to the major working stresses when the machine is in operation. Bending brakes require rugged construction, since they are subject to heavy loads and considerable abuse. The presence of an unnoticed piece of stock in the bottom of the die or the setting of the ram a little too close in its downstroke may introduce heavy overloads. Distortion of the frame and failure were experienced in the original types of brakes. The redesign, as shown in Fig. 5–4, was made on the basis of a sturdy product.

Fig. 5-4. Large all-welded press-brake frame machined for attachments.

The design of a press brake is purely a problem in deflection. Minimum deflections are necessary in order to obtain uniform bends throughout the length of the plate. The designer takes the maximum permissible deflection and designs the bed, ram, and frame to carry the maximum loads with an ample factor of safety.

Housings that had been simple steel plates in previous models are now enclosed box sections with deeper throats. The bed, an I-beam fabricated out of heavy plate and welded integral with the frame, replaces a single heavy plate section. The crowns are boxed in and not only take bearing thrusts but also are integral with the bed and give added rigidity to the entire frame. An automatic overload device disengages the clutch should the deflections in the frame become excessive. The net result of this redesign is a monolithic structure that provides maximum resistance to deflection and distortion.

Light Weight and Rigidity

Figure 5–5 shows the welded base for a precision machine. The chief requirements in design were maximum rigidity and minimum weight. Stiffness was developed by using many light cross-rib sections. These ribs were skip-welded. Tubing was used at joints where stiffeners crossed at sharp angles, to make for easier welding at the

Fig. 5-5. Base for a precision-type machine.

junctions. A strap was welded around the lower inside edge of the bed. Since the bottom edge required machining, the strap was secured by a fillet weld along the inside edge and also by 2-in. plug welds placed on about one-foot centers. The plug welds were added because a single fillet weld is very weak when the root is subjected to tensile stress.

A base of this type was stress-relieved, finish-machined, and stored for four years. Later it was checked and found to have changed less than 0.002 in. in any dimension. The base was then used without further processing of any kind. This example demonstrates that a proper stress relief of a welded structure permanently relieves all residual stresses resulting from forming and welding.

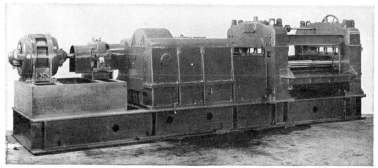

COURTESY WEAN ENGINEERING CO.

Fig. 5-6. Steel-mill plate-roller leveler.

Rolled Shapes Used in Low-Base Construction

A steel-mill plate-roller leveler is shown in Fig. 5–6. The low bed frame is constructed of wide-flange beams with outside stiffeners placed where continuity is required.

Styling

The appearance of a welded machine bed can be tremendously improved by simple design features. Figure 5–7, for example, shows a cold-rolling machine having a plain base of box construction with rounded corners. A streamlining effect has been created by simply cutting out parallel strips and backing up the opening with a bar. The use of a lighter tone of paint for the slots enhances the effect.

Flared Bottom

Figure 5–8 illustrates the use of a flared bottom that is easily formed in the press brake. Note the tie-down lugs welded into the flare.

Louver Doors and Slides

The louver door serves a dual purpose. It provides ventilation for the coolant reservoir and it adds to the appearance of the base.

COURTESY ETNA MACHINE CO.

Fig. 5-7. Modern-style bed for cold-rolling machine.

COURTESY ETNA MACHINE CO.

Fig. 5-8. Weldment illustrating use of a flared base.

The louver door is a stamping made in rather light metal with standard dies available for this work. The slide is S.A.E. 1045 steel and is welded integral with the bed.

Oil-Pan-Base Construction

An interesting type of oil-pan base is shown in Fig. 5–9. The bottom rail is bar stock. A ¼-in. plate is welded across the bottom to provide an oil reservoir. The side walls consist of ⅜-in. plate

COURTESY CLEVELAND TWIST DRILL CO.

Fig. 5-9. Base designed similar to the original casting, with a 40 per cent weight reduction.

formed in two sections. The sections are vee butt-welded, and all reinforcement is removed by grinding. The oil pan is formed in one piece. The corners are forged out of hot-rolled steel in a special die. The oil pan slopes toward the center drain. Heavy supporting blocks for the machinery are welded directly to the heavy frame structure. The pan is cut out at these points.

The weight of this bed was reduced about 40 per cent below the weight of a suitable cast-iron structure. The steel side wall was ⅜-in. thick where the casting had been ⅝-in., and the oil pan was reduced from ⅜ to ³⁄₁₆ in. in thickness.

Heavy Corner Fillet Welds

In Fig. 5–10, a heavy-walled seamless pipe is fitted into the design of a pump housing in rather pleasing style. This housing is fabricated of heavy plate. Outside corner fillet welds are used for the upper and lower housings, and the welds are ground to a uniform radius.

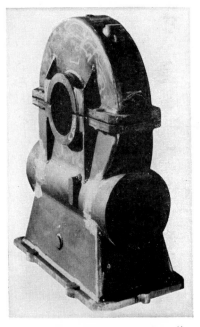

Fig. 5-10. Pump housing. The cylindrical sections of heavy-wall thickness are formed in two halves in a bulldozer. Note the bosses and lugs built to the contour of the weldment.

Pan-Bed Construction

The base for a large turret lathe is shown in Fig. 5–11. This pan has a built-in oil sump, and the bed is constructed to support the lathe. The pan proper consists of $3/16$-in. plate. The double-radius corners are formed and welded in place. The welds are visible in the photograph. The bottom rail is heavy and the frame is reinforced with U-shaped ribs formed in the brake. Note the tie-down lugs at the near end of the pan.

Heavy Box Construction

An all-welded multistage wiredrawing block is shown in Fig. 5–12. This base, of enclosed box construction, is about 22 ft. long

COURTESY WARNER AND SWASEY CO.

Fig. 5-11. Base for No. 4A turret lathe.

and weighs about 8 tons. The top bedplate and the far-side plate are constructed of $1\frac{1}{4}$-in. plate. Both are planed. Many of these bases have been fabricated successfully without stress relief.

COURTESY VAUGHN MACHINE CO.

Fig. 5-12. All-welded multistage wiredrawing block. The pipe projection at the right end is part of the cooling system fabricated into the bed.

Fig. 5-13. A plastic injection machine bed with pressure chamber built into base. The motor support is attached at the left.

COURTESY HALL MANUFACTURING CO.

Fig. 5-14. Support and oil sump for grinding aircraft-engine valves in the field.

Rounded Corners

A plastic injection machine is shown in Fig. 5–13. A pressure chamber is built into the bottom. This machine illustrates the excellent appearance that can be created in welded construction by the use of rounded corners.

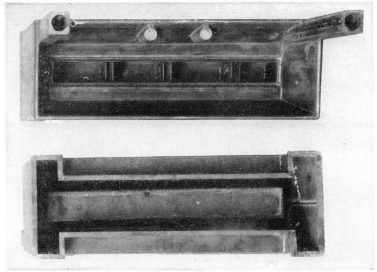

COURTESY HALL MANUFACTURING CO.

Fig. 5-15. Top and bottom views of the support shown in Fig. 5-14. Most of the welding is confined to the corners.

Plate Forming

Figures 5–14 and 5–15 show the base of a machine for grinding aircraft-engine valves. The base is constructed of $\frac{5}{16}$-in. plate and is a notable example of good plate-bending design. In this instance the designer used bending to the fullest extent and minimized welding. The result was a light rigid base at low cost. Figure 5–15 shows how the four sides were formed and then assembled and welded at the corners.

Light Metal Construction

A threading machine with a light base and oil pan of good design appears in Fig. 5–16. The plate is $\frac{3}{16}$ in. thick throughout.

COURTESY OSTER MANUFACTURING CO.

Fig. 5-16. Pipe-threading machine with an all-welded steel base. The louver door, a standard stamping design, adds considerably to the appearance of the weldment.

A bar, welded around the bottom to stiffen the frame, also adds to the appearance. Further stiffening is accomplished by plate bending and box design.

Fig. 5-17. A two-point press.

Heavy Welded Construction

An enclosed two-point press with welded tie-rod frame construction is shown in Fig. 5-17.

Engine Beds

The design of the Diesel-engine frame in Fig. 5-18 is interesting as an illustration of the efficient use of material and shape in creating maximum stiffness with minimum weight. The particular base shown is for a 12-cylinder engine and generator mounting. The welded crankcase is shown in Fig. 5-19. The openings are flanged to add extra stiffness to the plate. This assembly was fabricated to a tolerance in the overall dimensions of $\pm \frac{1}{16}$ in.

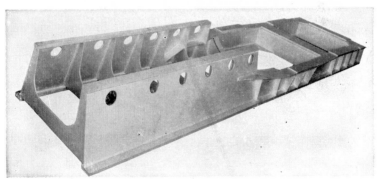

Fig. 5-18. Fabricated base for a 12-cylinder Diesel engine. Frames for marine use such as the type shown here are extremely light, considering the weight of the engine. Note the few crossribs. Great rigidity is obtained with light weight by using high side walls.

Figure 5–20 shows a 16-cylinder Diesel engine and generator mounted on a welded base.

COURTESY CLEVELAND DIESEL ENGINE DIVISION, GENERAL MOTORS CORP.

Fig. 5-19. All-welded steel crankcase for a 12-cylinder Diesel engine.

COURTESY CLEVELAND DIESEL ENGINE DIVISION, GENERAL MOTORS CORP.

Fig. 5-20. Diesel engine and generator set mounted on an all-welded steel base.

Elimination of Machining Operations

An electrical-control manufacturing company has developed greater economy by eliminating machining operations in the fabrication of machine frames. Among its products is an arc-welded DC

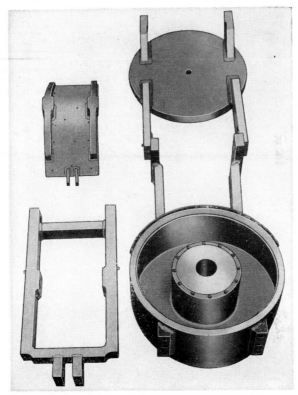

COURTESY CLARK CONTROLLER CO.

Fig. 5-21. Welded parts of a magnetic shoe brake, including magnet case, clapper, a brake shoe, and lever arm.

magnetic shoe brake designed for heavy duty applications, such as crane hoists, screw-downs, general mill auxiliaries, and similar applications where it is necessary to stop a DC or AC motor quickly and smoothly without severe shock to the connected mechanism.

The essential parts of this shoe brake are a frame, two lever arms, two shoes, and a clapper-type electromagnet made up of an armature plate and a magnet case and coil.

Because of the amount of machining that would be required on these parts if they were made of cast steel, one company designer was called upon to develop drawings for a completely welded unit.

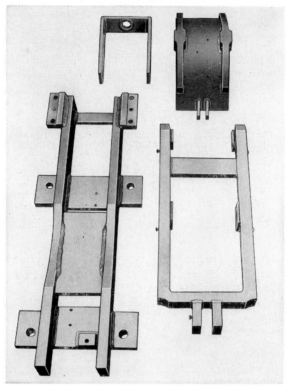

COURTESY CLARK CONTROLLER CO.

Fig. 5-22. Welded parts of a magnetic shoe brake, including the frame, lever arm, and brake shoe.

In the course of his studies he discovered that by using plate and bar stock (disregarding drilled and tapped holes that would have to be in both cast and welded units), all but five machining operations could be avoided. Elimination of 25 machining operations by use of weldments was the result.

Figures 5–21, 5–22, and 5–23 show this complete group of weldments. Notice that the frame and the two lever arms are made of bar stock. The magnet case ring is made of bar stock, as are the upright arms and the core. The back of the magnet case and the armature or clapper are flame-cut from plate. Rolled steel is used for the magnet in preference to cast steel because of added advantages in greater density and better magnetic quality. The brake-lining rivet holes are drilled in the flat sheet and then rolled

COURTESY CLARK CONTROLLER CO.

Fig. 5-23. Complete assembly of a magnetic shoe brake.

to shape to form the shoe. The remaining parts of the shoe are bar stock. All fabricated parts in this brake are hot-rolled mild steel. The brake drum used with this brake consists of a high-carbon-steel rim and mild hot-rolled-steel web and hub. Machine time is kept to a minimum, and rejections due to blowholes and shrinkage are eliminated.

The cost of the finished weldments is 28.7 per cent less than the cost of finished cast-steel parts. This saving, a result of eliminating machine work, was sufficient to assure the future of welded construction in this electrical-manufacturing plant.

Pan Base for Precision Machine

Figures 5–24 and 5–25 illustrate a pan base used on a multiple-spindle automatic machine. Figure 5–24 shows the base completely assembled, and Fig. 5–25 gives some idea of the interior construction. The contours were designed by the noted industrial artist Henry Dreyfuss, who also styled the rest of the machine.

COURTESY WARNER AND SWASEY CO.

Fig. 5-24. Finished pan base for a multiple-spindle automatic machine, with oil sump covers in place.

The main supporting members in the base, which is 16 in. high, are made of $\frac{3}{8}$-in. plate. The exterior contours, which do not contribute much to supporting the machine, are made of $\frac{3}{16}$-in. sheet. The base features pyramidal inside supports, which are intended to break up stress concentrations and also serve as baffles for the coolant as it flows back to the sump.

The strength of the base has been proved beyond question. Of the several hundred machines that have been produced, none have had any misalignment trouble. The base is not stress-relieved. It was felt that stress-relieving was not necessary, since the only machining necessary is a cleanup cut on the top surface and the drilling and tapping of some holes. Also, the base has such a deep section that it is able to stand the residual forces from fabricating as well as the forces from operating the machine.

A casting was originally designed for the machine, but it had a number of disadvantages. In the first place, it would have weighed about 4,500 lb. as compared to the welded-steel base weighing

COURTESY WARNER AND SWASEY CO.

Fig. 5-25. Pyramidal inside supports of the pan base shown in Fig. 5-24.

2,200 lb. The cost of the pattern would have been about $4000. Even with the excess weight, it is doubtful whether the casting would have been as stiff as the steel. Although it is generally accepted that cast iron machines more easily than steel, in this case the cast-iron design would require more machining stock, so that there would have been little or no saving in machining time. The cast-iron design would not have held as much coolant as the steel design. Moreover, its cleanout facilities would have been poor.

CHAPTER 6

Welding Specifications

Purpose of Specifying Welding

All welded seams should be definitely specified as to type, size, and continuity. The engineer who designs a weldment knows the nature of the loads and stresses as a result of his studies of the structure, and is in the best position to state the correct welding requirements. Any less than the required amount means that the structure is underwelded, whereas any welding in excess of the required amount means that the structure is overwelded.

The fabricator has no way of knowing just how much welding is required unless it is specified, and in cases of doubt he will probably put in continuous welds when skip welds would suffice. In most cases where there are no specifications, the fabricator will overweld to be on the safe side. The resultant extra cost may spell the failure of the project from a cost standpoint. If the fabricator uses ⅜-in. fillets where ¼-in. fillets are sufficient, the welding labor is double what it should be. Doubling the amount of welding will increase the shop cost of fabrication about 50 per cent and increase the total cost of fabrication approximately 15 per cent. These figures show that welding represents a large percentage of the total cost of fabrication and that fabrication should be under strict control.

The omission of a welding specification may result in failure of machine-base weldments that must withstand excessive pressure or working stresses. Take, for example, a press frame. The designer makes a stress analysis to determine the size of the various members required to develop the necessary strength and rigidity. In

such a structure, the amount of welding should be carefully estimated and specified by symbol. The stress analysis may indicate
that certain joints in the main frame units must be fully welded to
make the weld strength equal to the plate strength. On the other
hand, the outside bracing on the same structure may carry very
little stress, in which case it may be joined safely by light fillet
welds. If a structure of this type is fabricated by a commercial
weldery without knowledge of the use for which the structure is
intended, it is quite possible that certain highly stressed joints may
be underwelded, whereas the lightly stressed seams may be need-
lessly overwelded.

Following are two specific cases in which faulty specifications for
highly stressed weldments resulted in seam failure.

The first example was a vulcanizing unit used by the rubber
industry. The base was of ordinary box construction and weighed
about 6000 lb. The top bedplate was 1 in. thick and required a
finish. The design (Fig. 6–1) indicated a vee weld around the
upper edge of the base to join the top bedplate to the side walls.
This was poor design, because a partial vee weld was indicated on a
machined surface and was cut down in the machining process.
Perhaps the designer thought that a partial vee weld would be
sufficient, since the side walls were only $\frac{3}{8}$ in. thick. The drawing
failed to specify that this weldment should withstand steam pressure; and even though continuous welding was specified on the
drawing, nothing had been noted as to the size of the weld.

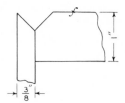

Fig. 6-1. Bedplate as
indicated on drawing.

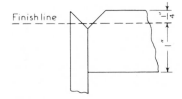

Fig. 6-2. Bedplate as fabricated.

Figure 6–2 shows how the weldment was prepared in the shop.
A 1¼-in. top bedplate was used to allow ¼ in. for machining. The
vee weld was made about ⅜ to ½ in. deep as shown. In machining
this base, it was found necessary to remove more than ¼ in.; and
when the base was tested under pressure, the seams leaked badly.

In analyzing this failure, it is apparent that a vee weld on a finished surface is poor design unless a full vee is specified, which should give ample weld irrespective of the amount of metal removed in machining. The designer made a grave error in failing to specify that the bed must withstand a definite steam pressure, since the fabricator must have this information in order to produce a satisfactory weld. The solution to this problem is presented in Fig. 6-3. The welding has been eliminated from the finished surface, and a full-section vee weld without reinforcement has been indicated at the side. This design provides a weld at least equal in strength to the 3⁄8-in. plate,

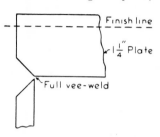

Fig. **6-3.** Solution to problem introduced in Figs. 6-1 and 6-2.

which is all that is necessary in developing a completely satisfactory joint. The proper design, plus adequate welding symbols, makes the work both definite and fool-proof.

The second case of weld seam failure resulting from faulty specification was as follows. In the early days of welded-base design for Diesel engines, double fillets were specified in the manner shown in Fig. 6-4. The 1⁄2-in. crossribs were welded to the 1⁄2-in.

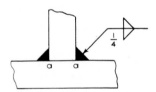

Fig. **6-4.** Double 1⁄4-in. fillet welds.

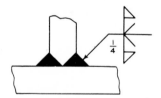

Fig. **6-5.** Double 1⁄4-in. bevel fillet welds.

side walls by means of 1⁄4-in. double fillets. For most types of service, this amount of welding would be ample. In marine service however, several weld failures resulted due to the effect of vibration and shock. For such a condition, the weld specified in Fig. 6–4 was at fault. Although it provided ample strength for normal loading, there was no continuity between points *a-a,* which were stress concentration points. Fatigue failures were eliminated by using a joint, as shown in Fig. 6–5. In a critical case of this kind, the welding symbol is the most practical means by which the designer can safely regulate the work of the weldery.

Welding Symbols

The American Welding Society has published a set of standardized symbols which are in use today by many designers and fabricators.[1] The symbols have been devised to describe the weld in complete detail, so that the welder will have no difficulty in following the plan and achieving the desired result.

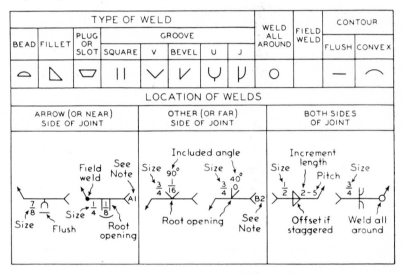

Fig. 6-6. Symbols for gas and arc welding.

Figure 6–6 shows how the system works. The same symbols are used for both gas and arc welding. The type of weld is indicated at the top of the diagram. These markings for the type of weld are used in conjunction with the arrows that show the weld locations, and other figures are used to specify the size of the weld and the continuity. The first symbol to the left describes a 7/8-in. single U-groove butt weld with a flush finish. The next symbol describes a square-opening butt joint with a single 1/4-in. weld. The root opening is 1/8 in., and the reinforcement is left on. This weld is to be

---

[1] *Standard Welding Symbols and Rules for Their Use,* American Welding Society, New York, 1947 ed.

continuous and made in the field. A1 refers to a note on the drawing. Both of these welds just described are on the near side toward which the arrow points. The third symbol from the left specifies a

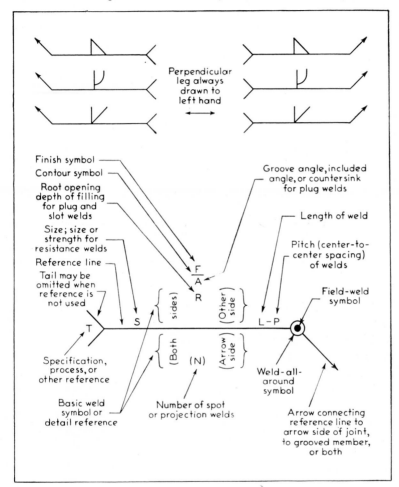

Fig. 6-7. Standard location of information on weld symbols.

full ¾-in. single vee weld with a 90-deg. included angle and a
¹⁄₁₆-in. root opening. The weld is to be continuous. The next
symbol describes a ¾-in. single vee weld with no root opening, and
B2 refers to a note on the drawing. These last two welds are for

the side of the joint opposite to where the arrow points, referred to as the "far side." The next symbol, the fifth from the left, describes a ½-in. double fillet weld. Skip welds are specified 2 in. long and 5 in. between centers, and the increments are to be equal and opposite. The last symbol indicates a ¾-in. double J butt weld all around.

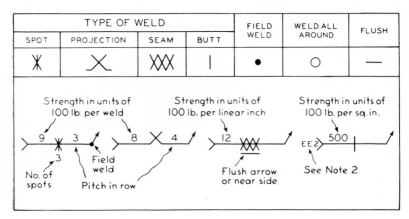

Fig. 6-8. Resistance welding symbols.

Figure 6–7 shows where the information is located with respect to the arrow.

Figure 6–8 shows the symbols used in describing the various types of resistance welding. The same system of identification by arrow as used for the arc and gas welds is fully described.

The 50 accompanying diagrams (pages 74–82) illustrate in detail how the various types of arc welds are indicated by means of welding symbols. The efficiency of each type of weld is described in relation to the ability of the weld to resist various types of stresses.

ARC WELD SYMBOLS

1. Closed Square Butt Joint

Penetration ¼ in., welded on near side only (arrow side). Normal re-enforcement. Low efficiency. Not suitable for fatigue or impact. Should not be used when bending tension can come on root of weld.

2. Closed Square Butt Joint

Welded one side. Complete penetration. Efficiency in static tension is dependent on degree of penetration. Not advisable for use in severe fatigue and impact with bending tension on root.

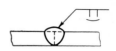

3. Closed Square Butt Joint

Penetration $\frac{1}{8}$ in. Welded on both sides. Normal re-enforcement. Relatively low efficiency in static loading. Should not be used in fatigue or impact.

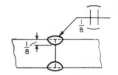

4. Closed Square Butt Joint

Penetration complete. Welded on both sides. Normal re-enforcement. Possibility of obtaining complete penetration should be checked before using this joint on important structures. High efficiency if penetration is complete.

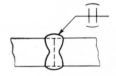

5. Open Square Butt Joint

Welded one side. $\frac{1}{8}$ in. penetration; $\frac{3}{16}$ in. root opening. Greater penetration possible than with a closed butt joint. Low efficiency in static loading. Should not be used in fatigue or impact, or when bending tension can come in root of weld.

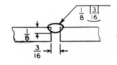

6. Open Square Butt Joint

$\frac{1}{8}$-in. root opening. Full penetration. Welded on both sides. Normal re-enforcement. Relatively high efficiency can be obtained if complete penetration is assured. Should not be used for severe fatigue and impact because of likelihood of flaws at root of weld.

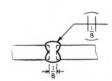

7. Open Square Butt Joint

Welded both sides. Incomplete penetration. Relatively low efficiency in static loading, dependent on ratio of weld throat to plate thickness. Should not be used in fatigue or impact.

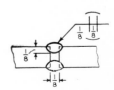

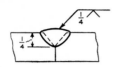

8. Vee Groove

Beveled ¼ in. Less than complete penetration, near side. Normal re-enforcement.

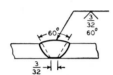

9. 60-Deg. Single Vee Groove

³⁄₃₂-in. root opening. Full penetration. Normal re-enforcement. Relatively high static efficiency obtainable. Should not be used when bending tension can exist at root of weld. Undesirable in fatigue and impact. Economical up to ⅝-in. plate. Better efficiency and production with proper backing.

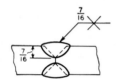

10. Double Vee Groove

Beveled ⁷⁄₁₆ in. (less than complete weld), both sides. Normal re-enforcement.

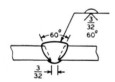

11. Single Vee Groove

Full penetration. Normal re-enforcement. Single bead applied to root side. High static efficiency. Economical up to ⅝-in. plate. With good penetration, good efficiency can be obtained in fatigue or impact; better if re-enforcements are removed.

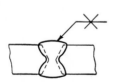

12. Double Vee Groove

Full penetration. Economical up to 1¾-in. plate. High static efficiency obtainable. Good efficiency in fatigue and impact if weld is properly prepared; better if re-enforcement is removed.

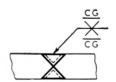

13. Double Vee Groove

Full penetration. Center chipped out. Welds ground flush both sides. High static efficiency. Economical up to 1¾-in. plate. Good efficiency in fatigue and impact.

14. DOUBLE VEE GROOVE

Same as 13 except that welds are finished approximately flush without recourse to any method of finishing.

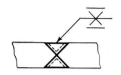

15. SINGLE U GROOVE

½ in. deep, near side. Incomplete penetration. Normal re-enforcement.

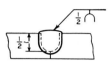

16. SINGLE U GROOVE

Welded one side, full penetration. High efficiency obtainable. Undesirable in severe fatigue or impact, or when bending tension can come on root of weld.

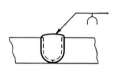

17. DOUBLE U GROOVE

Near side ¾ in. deep. Far side ⅜ in. deep. Normal re-enforcement.

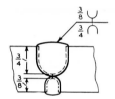

18. SINGLE U GROOVE

Welded both sides. Economical in ½-in. plate and up. Highest static efficiencies obtainable. If quality is good, high efficiency in fatigue and impact; higher if re-enforcements are removed.

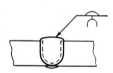

19. DOUBLE U GROOVE

Full penetration. Highest static efficiency obtainable. Most economical in the heaviest thicknesses. Chipping of root easy. If quality is good, high efficiency in fatigue and impact; higher if re-enforcements are removed.

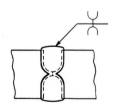

20. SINGLE J GROOVE

Welded one side, full penetration. High static efficiency. Undesirable in severe fatigue and impact, and when bending tension can come on root of weld. Economical in ½-in. plate and up, one member grooved.

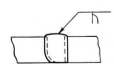

21. Single J Groove

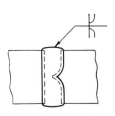

Welded both sides, full penetration. Highest static efficiencies obtainable. Chipping of root easy. High efficiency in fatigue and impact if quality is good. Economical in $\frac{1}{2}$-in. plate and up.

22. Double J Groove

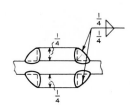

Full penetration. Highest static efficiency obtainable. High efficiency in fatigue and impact if quality is good. Chipping of root not so easy as for doube U groove. Most economical in heaviest thicknesses.

23. Open Double-Strapped Butt Joint

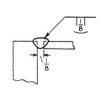

Joint capable of developing high static efficiency, depending on size of welds used. Excess weight of straps undesirable. Stress concentration bad in fatigue and impact. Not so economical as butt joint.

24. Open Square-Groove Corner Joint

Relatively high efficiency in shear. Should not be used in fatigue or impact, or when bending tension can occur in root of weld. Direct tension on either member can cause bending tension at root.

25. Open Square-Groove Corner Joint Fillet-Welded

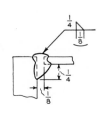

High efficiency in static loading. Undesirable in severe fatigue and impact.

26. Single Vee Corner Joint

Relatively high efficiencies in shear. Should not be used in fatigue and impact, or when bending tension can occur in root of weld.

27. SINGLE VEE CORNER JOINT FILLET-WELDED

High efficiencies obtainable. Not desirable in severe fatigue and impact on account of stress concentrations at toes of fillets.

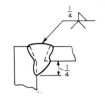

28. OUTSIDE SINGLE-BEVEL CORNER JOINT FILLET-WELDED

High efficiencies. Not desirable in severe fatigue and impact, on account of stress concentration at toes of fillets. Economical up to ⅝ in.

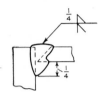

29. DOUBLE-BEVEL CORNER JOINT

High efficiency in static shear. Chipping of root difficult. Neither member should be subjected to severe tension because of concentrations of stress at the corner. Economical above ½ in.

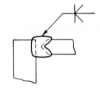

30. SINGLE U CORNER JOINT

High efficiency in static shear. Undesirable in fatigue and impact, or where bending tension can come on root of weld. Direct tension on either member can cause bending tension on root. Economical above ½ in.

31. SINGLE U CORNER JOINT FILLET-WELDED

Highest efficiencies in static shear. Chipping of root easy. Undesirable in severe fatigue and impact because of stress concentration at toes of fillet. Economical in ½-in. plate and up.

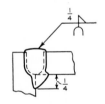

32. DOUBLE J. CORNER JOINT

High efficiency in static shear. Chipping of root rather difficult. Neither member should be subjected to severe tension because of stress concentration at the corner. Not advisable in severe fatigue and impact. Most economical in heaviest thicknesses.

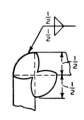

33. DOUBLE FILLET-WELDED CORNER JOINT

High efficiencies in static shear. Good efficiency in static bending. Undesirable in severe fatigue and impact on account of stress concentration at toes of fillet. Economical in smaller plate sizes.

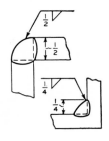

34. OUTSIDE AND INSIDE SINGLE FILLET-WELDED CORNER JOINT

Capable of high efficiency in static bending with bending tension on the face. Will fail at low values if root of weld is subjected to tension. Direct tension on either member will subject the root of weld to tension. High efficiency in static shear. Not economical when fillets are of large size. Not for fatigue and impact.

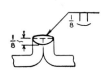

35. SQUARE-EDGE JOINT

Should not be used when either member is subjected to direct tension. Should not be used when joint is subjected to bending, so that bending tension exists at root of weld. High efficiency in shear. Should not be used in impact or fatigue. Economical for routine production work.

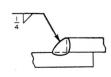

36. SINGLE FILLET-WELDED LAP JOINT

Should not be used when root of weld can be subjected to bending. Will distort out of line when functioning as an expansion joint (rotate under tension). High efficiency in shear. Easy to fit. Economical in moderate thicknesses. Should not be used in fatigue and impact.

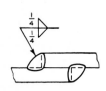

37. DOUBLE FILLET-WELDED LAP JOINT

Can develop high efficiency in tension when lap is 5 tons or more. Undesirable in fatigue and impact. Will distort out of line functioning as an expansion joint (rotate under tension). High efficiency in shear. Easy to fit. Economical in moderate thicknesses.

38. SINGLE FILLET WELD

¼-in. equal legs, weld continuous. Capable of developing high efficiency in static bending with bending tension on face. Will fail at low values if root of weld is subjected to tension, or if perpendicular member is subjected to direct tension. Capable of developing high strength in shear.

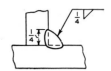

39. SINGLE FILLET WELD

Same as 38. Illustrating how the designer designates a special finish which is to be accomplished by mechanical means, (1) calls for a convex finish by grinding (G), (2) for a flat finish by grinding, and (3) for a flat finish by machining (M).

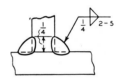

40. DOUBLE FILLET WELD

¼-in. equal legs, 2-in. welds on 5-in. centers, increments opposite. Capable of developing high efficiency in static tension, compression, shear, bending. Inadvisable in severe fatigue and impact because of stress concentration at roots of fillets.

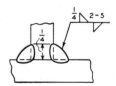

41. DOUBLE FILLET WELD

¼-in. equal legs, 2-in. welds on 5-in. centers, increments staggered.

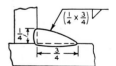

42. SINGLE FILLET WELD

¼-in. and ¾-in. legs, continuous weld.

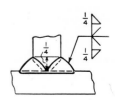

43. DOUBLE-BEVEL FILLET JOINT

¼-in. bevels and ¼-in. fillets outside, continuous. Highest efficiency can be obtained in static tension, shear, compression, and bending; good efficiency in fatigue and impact. Economical up to 1-in. plate.

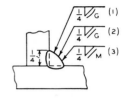

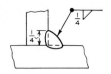

44. Single Fillet Weld

¼-in. near side, continuous weld. To be made in the field.

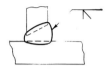

45. Single-Bevel Tee Joint

High static efficiency in shear. Undesirable in fatigue and impact. Should not be used where bending tension can occur in root of weld. Economical up to ⅝-in. plate.

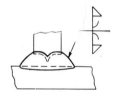

46. Double Fillet-Welded Double J Tee Joint

Highest efficiency in static tension, compression, bending, and shear; good efficiency in fatigue and impact. Economical in the heaviest thicknesses.

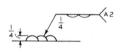

47. Top Surface Pad

¼-in. beads. A2 refers to a note in the specifications requiring the use of a special type of electrode for this hard-surface work.

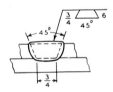

48. Plug Weld

¾-in.-diameter hole in top plate. Sides tapered, total angle 45 deg. Welds spaced on 6-in. centers.

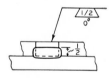

49. Plug Weld

1-in.-diameter hole, perpendicular sides, ½-in. depth.

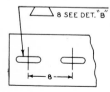

50. Slot Weld

Symbol on drawing refers to a detailed sketch showing the exact dimensions of the slot. The orientation is shown on the drawing; spaced on 8-in. centers.

Specifying Material and Workmanship

A series of drawings should describe the weldment fully and leave no doubt as to the material and workmanship desired. A typical specification is given below.

MATERIAL SPECIFICATION

1. The mark f1 indicates machine-finish rough.
2. The mark f2 indicates machine-finish smooth.
3. Quality: Sections composing a weldment shall be commercially straight, flat, clean, smooth, and free from seams, laminations, blisters, scale, and other injurious defects. The weldment shall finish to the dimensions shown on the drawing.
4. Material: Welding-quality steel.
5. Chemical analysis:

$$C \quad \ldots\ldots 0.13-0.25$$
$$Mn \quad \ldots\ldots 0.60 \text{ max.}$$
$$Ph \quad \ldots\ldots 0.04 \text{ max.}$$
$$S \quad \ldots\ldots 0.05 \text{ max.}$$

The following SAE and AISI compositions conform to the above analysis:

SAE 1015 and 1020
AISI C1014, C1015, and C1017
AISI C1020, C1021, and C1023

6. Physical properties: Not required.
7. Heat-treatment: Stress-relieve.
8. Any special notes in regard to precautions, rejections, and so on.

It is not necessary to describe stress relief, since the treatment is standard and well understood by the commercial weldery. If sandblasting is required in cleaning up after stress-relieving, it should be noted on the drawing. The standard procedure used by most welderies in cleaning up weldments is to go over them thoroughly with a motor-driven wire brush that removes all the loose scale, oxide spatter, and slag. Outside vee welds are ground flush. This cleaning procedure should be specified on the drawing in a note as follows:

All loose scale, oxide, weld slag, and spatter should be removed from the weldment by means of a motor-driven wire brush. Rough welds and edges should be smoothed with a grinder. All vee butt welds should be ground flush with the plate.

Amount of Welding to Specify

Oil-storage tanks, reservoirs, and air-pressure chambers should be continuously welded. Two light fillet welds are always preferable to a single heavy fillet in order to prevent leaks. Any machine base that has an inner oil compartment should be double-welded or kerosene-tested. Double welding is almost certain to be oil-tight and requires no test.

All visible welds on machinery should be continuous, even though skip welding might be sufficient in strength, as the continuous weld gives a finished appearance to the structure and makes it look more rugged. Inside bracing and ribbing can often be skip-welded.

Machine-base construction generally involves box construction and a preponderance of tee fillet welding. The stress analysis will indicate the correct size of plates and ribs to be used. The type of weld is selected from the arc weld symbols shown on pages 74–82, based upon the nature of the stresses encountered. For static loads, stress concentration is not a serious consideration, and the fillet weld (40) is satisfactory. For light machine bases consisting of $1/4$-in. plates or less, a single tee fillet weld is ample; but for stiffer plates, $3/8$ in. and greater in thickness, the double tee fillet weld should always be used, because the single fillet weld is very weak when the plates are bent, thereby subjecting the root of the weld to tension. The outside plates of the machine bed should have continuous fillet welds, whereas the inside fillets may be continuous or skip-welded, depending upon the load.

There are varying degrees of static loading, requiring consideration of the different types of joint design. Excessive costs may result from poor design and selection of joints. With highly stressed parts, where the loading may approach the yield point of the material, fillet and butt welds must have good penetration. The quality of the weld—reinforcement and appearance—should be closely controlled. The joints should be scarfed to obtain full penetration where necessary, and fit-up tolerances should be such as to obtain top-quality welds. The parts of a weldment that are not subjected to high stresses, merely supporting the structure in a certain shape, should be welded speedily and at low cost.

In certain structures developed to withstand high loading without deformation, the seam welds may often be made very light in section, since the main factor is rigidity and there is very little stress per square inch except in the extreme fibers. Since deflection is mainly a function of the moment of inertia, welding done in the center of the plate near the neutral axis has very little effect upon rigidity. In most butt welds, much less than 100 per cent fusion is necessary. Fillet welds also can be light. In most cases plates up to 1 in. in thickness do not have to be scarfed at all, and plates over 1 in. need very little scarfing.

In Fig. 6–9, the inside welds are made 2 in. long on 5-in. centers for the rib as well as for the inside seams of the outer plates. Where the static loading is heavy and strong welds are required, the inside welds should be continuous. Quarter-inch fillet welds should be ample for ½-in. plate, and ⅜-in. fillets for ¾-in. plate. Quarter-inch or ⅜-in. fillet welds are generally sufficient for bosses, slides, bearing plates and similar components.

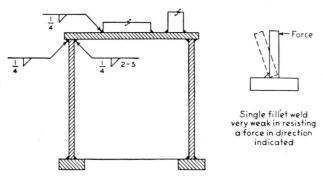

Single fillet weld very weak in resisting a force in direction indicated

Fig. 6-9. Cross section of a welded base of box construction.

For dynamic loads and in bases subject to considerable vibration, stress concentration becomes a major consideration, and continuous bevel fillet joints, as shown by weld (43), should be used throughout.

For heavy plate construction subject to fatigue, the double fillet-welded double J tee joint (46), which requires less weld metal, may be used.

A single lap seam, as shown in weld (36), is satisfactory for light metal up to ¼ in. Above this thickness, the double fillet-welded lap joint (37) should be used, since the single lap seam is weak when bent, thus subjecting the root of the weld to tension.

When corner welds are specified in heavy plate [see weld (34)], the designer should indicate that the weld must be well rounded to provide an ample throat section, as indicated in Fig. 6–10.

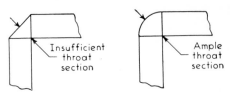

Fig. 6-10. Outside single fillet-welded corner joint.

In any joint between plates of different thickness, the throat section or the combined throat sections of the welds should never exceed the thickness of the lighter plate, even where the weld must be as strong as the plate. It is a case of no chain being stronger than its weakest link.

Vee welds in pressure vessels, and machine weldments subject to considerable vibration and fatigue stress, should have a flat finish specified with very little reinforcement, in order to avoid a stress concentration at the edge of the reinforcement.

Structural steel assemblies are rarely welded continuously, because so much welding is not required. The users of such materials are accustomed to discontinuities in the form of bolts and rivets. In transposing riveted construction into welded construction, the designer finds that a small amount of welding is required to match the shearing strength of the rivets. In a riveted design, the location of the rivets is just as important as their size and number, and all three are specified. In similar fashion, the designer of welded structural steel must specify the size, length, and exact location of each weld.

Specifying Types of Electrodes, Number of Passes, and the Amperage

Generally, the designer is not concerned with the technique of welding when the fabrication work is done by a commercial weldery outside his own plant. He is concerned about the amount of welding and the size of the welds, but he leaves it to the weldery engineers to decide how the job should be done. Each weldery has developed a welding technique of its own; for example, it may have a preference for automatic or for manual operation, and it will have made decisions on the proper type and size of electrode to use, the proper type of weld, the best amperage to use in each case, the number of passes, and the size and location of each pass. Furthermore, the commercial weldery knows from experience the best procedure to follow in assembly and welding. These are all important economic factors to the weldery but are of no direct consequence to the designer.

Of course there are exceptions. A company may fabricate its own machinery as well as design it. If the weldments are produced in duplicate parts on a large scale, the welding procedure will most likely be standardized. In such cases, the engineers will make a thorough study of each weldment to determine the most economical welding procedure that will satisfy the requirements. The designer will then specify these details, the size and type of electrode, the number of passes, and the amperage, so that the operation is fully described to the welding operator. In addition, the designer may also specify the procedure to be followed in assembling the weldment.

An example of a welding specification that includes a description of the electrode and other welding details is shown in Fig. 6–11. This symbol indicates that a $\frac{3}{16}$-in. continuous fillet weld

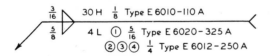

Fig. 6-11. Welding electrode specified.

is to be made on the far side of the joint in three passes in the overhead position using $\frac{1}{8}$-in. Type E6010 electrodes at 110 amp. On the near side, the designer has specified a $\frac{5}{8}$-in. continuous fillet weld made in the longitudinal position in four passes using a $\frac{5}{16}$-in. E6020 electrode at 325 amp. for the first pass and $\frac{1}{4}$-in. E6012 electrodes at 250 amp. for passes 2, 3, and 4.

Tables 6–1 and 6–2 are a condensation of "Tentative Specifications For Iron and Steel Arc Welding Electrodes." These specifications were prepared jointly by the American Welding Society (A.W.S.) and the American Society for Testing Materials

TABLE 6-1

Types of Heavy Covered Arc-welding Electrodes Used in the Fabrication of Weldments

A.W.S. classi-fication	Positions	General description	All weld-metal tension		
			Ult., p.s.i.	Yield, p.s.i.	% elong. in 2 in.
E6010	F, V, OH, H[1]	For use only with DC (electrode positive). Known as ALL POSITION, REVERSED POLARITY. Type $3/16''$ and smaller used for vertical and overhead. Penetrative arc, patchy slag, and flat bead	60M[2] 62M	47M 52M	27SR[3] 22NSR[4]
E6011	F, V, OH, H	AC and DC (electrode positive). Known as ALL-POSITION AC ROD. Same as E6010	60M 62M	47M 52M	27SR 22NSR
E6012	F, V, OH, H	AC and DC (electrode negative). Known as GENERAL PURPOSE ROD, POOR FIT-UP. $3/16''$ and smaller for vertical and over-head. Less penetrative than E6010. Convex bead	60M 62M	47M 52M	27SR 22NSR
E6013	F, V, OH, H	AC and DC (electrode negative). Known as GENERAL PURPOSE, LIGHT GAUGE. Characteristics similar to E6012	60M 62M	47M 52M	27SR 22NSR
E6020	H fillets	AC and DC (electrode negative). Known as HORIZONTAL FILLETS ROD. Concave bead. For vee or groove welding. Fillets very smooth. Hot-type rod. Full slag	60M 65M	47M 52M	30SR 25NSR
E6030	Flat	AC or DC (either polarity). Known as DEEP GROOVES ROD. Quite similar to E6020 but more fluid. Less slag. Designed for narrow deep grooves			

[1] F = flat, V = vertical, OH = overhead, H = horizontal.
[2] M = 1000.
[3] SR = stress relief.
[4] NSR = no stress relief.

(A.S.T.M.). They describe heavy covered (shielded) metal arc-welding electrodes for the welding of carbon and low-alloy steels of weldable quality.

Conclusion

In this chapter, the importance of specifying the weld has been emphasized from the standpoint of strength and economy. There is another important reason for definite welding specifications. Should the designer or buyer of weldments send out unspecified

TABLE 6-2

Types of High-tensile Heavy Covered Electrodes Used in Welding
Low-Alloy High-Strength Steels

Tensile series	A.W.S. classi-fication No.	Treatment of welded specimen	Tension test requirements of material deposited from 5/32″ to 5/16″ electrode (inclusive)		
			Tensile strength min., p.s.i.	Yield point min., p.s.i.	Elongation in 2 in., min. %
70,000 p.s.i.	E7010	SR	70,000	57,000	2ʑ
	E7011	SR	70,000	57,000	22
	E7012	SR	70,000	57,000	18
	E7020	SR	70,000	57,000	25
	E7030	SR	70,000	57,000	25
80,000 p.s.i.	E8010	SR	80,000	67,000	19
	E8011	SR	80,000	67,000	19
	E8012	SR	80,000	67,000	16
	E8020	SR	80,000	67,000	22
	E8030	SR	80,000	67,000	22
90,000 p.s.i.	E9010	SR	90,000	77,000	17
	E9011	SR	90,000	77,000	17
	E9012	SR	90,000	77,000	14
	E9020	SR	90,000	77,000	20
	E9030	SR	90,000	77,000	20
100,000 p.s.i.	E10010	SR	100,000	87,000	16
	E10011	SR	100,000	87,000	16
	E10012	SR	100,000	87,000	13
	E10020	SR	100,000	87,000	18
	E10030	SR	100,000	87,000	18

Note: The coating on the E6010 electrode corresponds to that on the E7010,
the E8010, and so on.

blueprints to several commercial welderies and request price quota-
tions, the estimates will most likely vary over a wide range because
of different interpretations of the amount of welding required. For
example, one weldery may consider 3/8-in. fillets sufficient for a
job, whereas another company submits a lower bid based on 1/4-in.
fillets. If 3/8-in. fillets actually are required and the bid goes to the
company submitting the lower estimate, the weldment may prove
to be unsatisfactory. Specifying the welding and other important

details places the job on a uniform basis that is readily under-stood and interpreted in the same manner by all bidding welderies, and the designer is assured of having the fabrication done correctly at minimum cost.

CHAPTER 7

Weldery Procedure

Types of Welderies

There are two types of organizations engaged in the manufacture of welded machine bases: the commercial weldery and the plant weldery. The commercial weldery commands a position in industry similar to that of the independent foundry; it supplies welded machine bases and machine parts to the machine-tool builder just as the foundry supplies castings. Relatively few builders of machinery find it economical to maintain either foundries or welderies of their own, and consequently most of them farm out their machine-base work to specializing companies equipped with all the modern devices for maximum economical operation.

The commercial weldery is equipped with machinery for shearing, sawing, bending, rolling, flame-cutting, assembling, positioning, handling, heat-treating, and sandblasting. Furthermore, because of the diversified nature of the work, the weldery is able to absorb and utilize a large part of the scrap, which often amounts to as much as 20 per cent of the gross material used. The weldery carries a staff of welding and structural engineers who, in cooperation with the design staff of the customer's plant, carry out the close coordination necessary for successful design and construction.

The plant weldery operates as the fabricating division of a large machinery manufacturing company, the work usually being confined to the company's own products. The manufacturing methods used by the commercial weldery and the plant weldery are similar, although the plant weldery handles only a few types of bases and hence is in a better position to standardize production methods.

The designer should be sufficiently familiar with the process of fabricating machine bases by arc welding to be able to visualize its possibilities and limitations.

Template and Bill of Material

The procedure of fabricating machinery frames or weldments generally follows a fixed pattern. When the weldery receives an order, the blueprints are given a shop number. A special office folder is marked with this number, and all activities relating to this job reach this folder in future operations. The blueprints are then studied carefully. If no unusual problems are involved, they are turned over to the template shop, which then decides upon the procedure of fabrication and prepares the necessary templates and a master bill of material covering all parts to go into the job. This is important work, since the success of the whole operation depends upon the proper choice of methods and accurate layout work. The templates for flame-cut shapes and for bent shapes are generally full-scale drawings made on heavy cardboard, and the bill of material shows the exact size to which each piece is to be cut and how it is to be prepared. For example, if a certain element is to be flame-cut to an irregular pattern, the bill of material will state the thickness of the plate and specify "Cut to template." A plate that is to be bent will be specified "Bend to template." In such designs involving unusual problems, the templates and the bill of material are both prepared by the engineering department.

Component Parts of a Weldment

The elements usually making up a weldment are listed as follows:

(1) *Plain material:* Either sheared, slow-speed saw-cut, friction saw-cut, or flame-cut to size.

(2) *Plates:* Flame-cut to template.

(3) *Elements:* Cut to size and then rolled or formed to template.

(4) *Special items:* Stampings, forgings, steel castings, pipe fittings, tubing, screens, hinges, louver doors, and so on.

Preparation of Materials

A number of processes are used in preparing the various components. A high-speed friction saw is used for cutting rolled sections such as angles, channels, beams, tees, zees, and piping. Plates up to 1 in. in thickness can be sheared. A rotary saw cuts small rounds and bars for pads and bosses. Angles are cut to length in a special angle shear.

"Burning" is the fabricators' shop term for oxyacetylene flame-cutting. Plates used as the walls, partitions, and pads of machine bases are burned to size when the thickness exceeds about ½ in. Heavy rectangular plates are burned to size with a tractor-type machine, and irregular and circular shapes are burned with a pantograph unit. Circles are also cut with special circle-burning machines. The flame-cut shape is such an important item in welding fabrication that Chapter 9 is devoted to that special subject.

The bent shape, usually formed in a press brake, is another component given extensive discussion in Chapter 10, Forming of Metals.

Plate rolls are used in forming bands and cylinders. Rings or flanges are usually edge-rolled in a special bar-bending machine.

Fit-up and Tack Welding

After the materials have been prepared, they are transported to the assembly table. This is a large cast-iron bed with T-slots in the surface to which tie bolts can be attached to hold the machine base in place while it is being set up and tack-welded. The fit-up men must interpret the drawing correctly and lay out the pieces in proper relationship and alignment. Tack welders work with them and tack the members sufficiently so that the final assembly can be moved as a unit to another location for the final welding. The fit-up men must frequently check all surfaces that are to be machined and make certain that they will clean up properly.

Finish Welding

After assembly work is completed, the weldment is picked up by crane and set down on a positioner or on a welding table. From this point on, the work is in the hands of welding operators who proceed to fill out the seams according to specification. The work is frequently inspected by the foreman of the department.

Improvements in the methods of manufacturing weldments have kept pace with the advances made in arc welding and also with the increased demand for welded products. The chief production improvements have been in jig and fixture design and in the use of positioners.

Jigs and Fixtures

A welding jig is a device capable of holding in definite relationship the component parts to be welded into an assembly. A fixture is similar to a jig, except that it permits changing the position of the work during the actual welding so as to place the seam in a plane convenient to the operator at all times.

A large percentage of the machine bases that are fabricated by the commercial weldery are not adapted to assembly by using jigs and fixtures, either because the size of the base is too great or because the quantities are insufficient to warrant the design and construction of special assembly and holding devices. When sufficient units of a single type are fabricated on a continuous production schedule, the weldery will undoubtedly develop special jigs and fixtures for greater economy. The plant weldery is generally well "jigged up" to fabricate on a continuous basis.

The setup or fit-up time represents a large percentage of the total time required to fabricate a weldment. The various components are fitted together, one by one in tailor fashion, on an assembly table. The assembly must be frequently checked for straightness and alignment, and the process is slow at best. If a fixture of proper design is available, this same weldment can be set up in much less time, since the fixture automatically locates key points and takes care of size and alignment. Consequently, the fit-up crew can proceed with greater assurance and speed. The fixture also prevents distortion during the process of welding. With these advantages available, the weldery will always consider the design and construction of a jig or fixture if conditions are the least bit favorable.

In designing a jig it should be kept in mind that the main purpose is to shorten fit-up time. The design should be light, positive in action, and easy and smooth in operation. The weld locations must be kept accessible. It is customary to keep the threaded portions of screws and bolts either covered by a guard or coated with grease to protect them from weld spatter.

One of the most commonly used jigs is the angle for placing pipe sections in true alignment.

A cone is a positive locating device for a piece of tubing, and a cup is ideal for a solid round (Fig. 7–1).

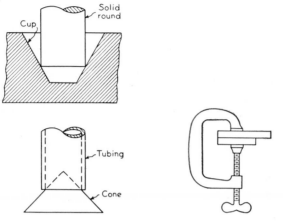

Fig. 7-1. Locating devices.   **Fig. 7-2.** C clamp.

The C-clamp is used perhaps more than any other device by the average weldery for miscellaneous jig work. (Fig. 7–2).

A commonly used fixture is the spinner type, which is easily constructed and is manually operated. It consists of a light steel

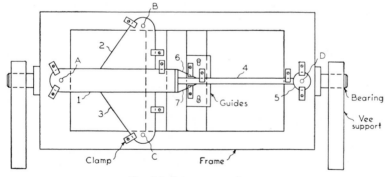

Fig. 7-3. Spinner-type fixture.

frame on which the work is assembled and welded. At each end of the frame there is a short axle or pivot that fits into supporting legs. The frame is free to swing into any position and may be locked. The frame and the work attached to it are well balanced for easy manipulation. Figure 7–3 shows a fixture of the spinner type with a weldment in position. This particular fixture is used for both assembling and welding. In all fixture-design work, the

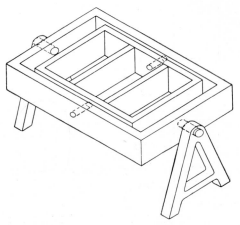

Fig. 7-4. Double spinner.

essential points or dimensions that must be controlled are determined first. Drilled holes are excellent locating points, as indicated on the drawing. The weldment consists of parts 1 to 6 inclusive. Holes *A, B, C,* and *D* are essential in locating points. Hold-down lugs are operated at these same points. Guides are added to locate parts 4 and 6. Several clamps are needed to secure these parts during welding.

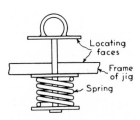

Fig. 7-5. Spring clamp.

Figure 7–4 illustrates a spinner-type fixture that revolves in both directions.

The jig screw latch and the thumb nut are commonly used for attaching weldments to the jig. A spring type of clamp is also common (Fig. 7–5).

Figure 7–6 shows heavy weldments under fabrication on hand-operated spinner-type positioners.

Weldments that are too long for positioning are picked up with a crane and set down against a beam or block to position the seams for trough-welding (Fig. 7–7).

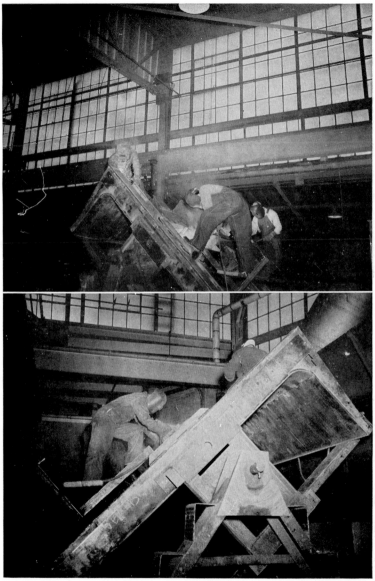

COURTESY EUCLID ROAD MACHINERY CO.

Fig. 7-6. Fabricating heavy dump-truck bodies on hand-operated spinner-type positioners.

Fig. 7-7. Trough-welding seams of weldments too long for available positioner equipment.

Figure 7–8 shows a small subassembly jig for tubular parts. The operations include assembly, tack welding, and finish welding. Figure 7–9 shows a large jig used for both tack and finish welding of the final assembly.

COURTESY WARNER AND SWASEY CO.

Fig. 7-8. Small subassembly jig for tubular parts.

Welding Positioner

The weldery tries to carry out all welding operations in the trough or the downhand position in order to produce better welds of smoother appearance at greater welding speed and less cost. Flat welding gives superior bead contour and design. It is almost entirely free of undercutting tendencies, whereas other positions demand greater skill on the part of the operator. An undercut weld gives high stress concentration at the edge of the weld; this condition is undesirable in all types of weldments, particularly in cases

COURTESY WARNER AND SWASEY CO.

Fig. 7-9. Large jig used for tack-welding radar parts in final assembly.

where impact and fatigue stresses are encountered. The trough weld is nicely concaved, whereas the off-position weld is very likely convex, a condition also causing high stress concentration.

Fabricators in general have accepted the welding positioner and consider it valuable in the modern production plant because it avoids many delays and much work handling.

According to old-style production methods, the weldery made use of both cranes and men in positioning heavy weldments. If the crane and the helpers were engaged when the time arrived to make a change in the position of the weldment, the welding operators were forced to wait for help. In many large weldments of complicated design, frequent changes in position are often required, since the welds must be distributed in order to avoid distortion. By avoiding delays, the modern positioner has enabled welderies to increase their production in some instances as much as 50 per cent. The work hazards are also materially reduced. After the weldment is once secured to the positioner, there is no further handling except by the machine itself.

Most positioners on the market provide the following features: (1) the table may be tilted 135 deg. from the horizontal position,

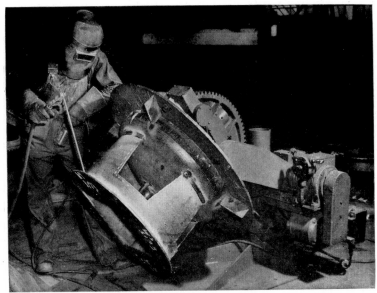

COURTESY CULLEN-FRIESTEDT CO.

Fig. 7-10. A welding positioner of 2,500 lb. capacity with a portable base.

(2) the table will rotate 360 deg., (3) the table height is adjustable, and (4) the table may be removed for direct attaching of a special jig or fixture.

Figure 7–10 shows a positioner of 2500 lb. capacity with a portable base. The table-tilting and -rotating mechanisms are power operated. The table is shown tilted 135 deg. from the horizontal position.

Figure 7–11 shows a positioner of 6000 lb. capacity with a column-in-floor base, power-operated table-tilting mechanism, and power-operated variable-speed table-rotation mechanism. The column is mounted in the floor and is raised or lowered by crane to the desired height, where it is locked in position.

COURTESY CULLEN-FRIESTEDT CO.

Fig. 7-11. A welding positioner of 6,000 lb. capacity with a column-in-floor base.

Figure 7–12 shows a positioner of 20,000 lb. capacity. It has a portable base, a power-operated table-tilting mechanism, and a power-operated constant-speed table-rotation mechanism.

Figure 7–13 shows a base for a steel-mill manufacturing unit. This base weighs about 5000 lb. and is 20 in. high, 4½ ft. wide, and 19½ ft. long. It is fabricated of ½-in. plate. The positioner is electrically driven and has a capacity of 7 tons.

Internal Stresses

As weld metal is deposited in a seam, it is suddenly quenched from a very high temperature (approximately 8000° F.), and the metal tends to shrink in volume. This shrinkage is resisted by the

COURTESY CULLEN-FRIESTEDT CO.

Fig. 7-12. A welding positioner of 20,000 pounds capacity with a portable base.

parent metal adjacent to the seam. If the shrinkage is not fully resisted, distortion results. Heavy rigid members do not distort readily, with the result that internal stresses are set up in the plate members. These stresses may vary considerably from one part of the structure to another, reaching high values. The strain gauge has been used to determine the nature and distribution of such stresses. If a stressed structure is machined, the removal of metal from a given section will upset the equilibrium, causing probable distortion and making proper machining impossible.

Heat-treatment is used for the relief of stresses. This particular heat-treatment is termed "stress relief" and must not be confused with normalizing and annealing. In a stress-relief treatment, the

COURTESY REPUBLIC STRUCTURAL IRON WORKS.

Fig. 7-13. Positioned fabrication of all-welded base for a steel-mill side trimmer.

structure is heated to about 1200° F., a temperature below the critical range. At this temperature there is no change in the grain structure, but there is a complete relieving of the stresses. The normalizing and annealing temperatures are above the critical range and produce changes in the grain structure as well as stress relief. For low-carbon steels, a very heavy scale forms if the temperature greatly exceeds the stress-relief range. This scale can be very troublesome in machining operations if the temperature is excessive. The scale obtained at ordinary stress-relieving temperatures is light and not troublesome.

Stress Relief

Many weldments that are machined to a finish are given a standard stress-relieving heat-treatment that is sometimes specified as follows:

Increase the temperature of the oven at the rate of 100°F. per hour to 1150°F. plus or minus 25°F. Hold at this temperature for two hours for sections up to 1 in. in thickness with an added ½ hr. for each 1 in. additional section; that is, 5 hr. for a section 6 in. thick. Cool at the rate of 100°F. per hour down to 250°F. or less in the furnace.

The stress-relieving treatment accomplishes a dual purpose: (a) any residual stresses set up in the members as a result of cold-bending, flame-cutting, or welding are definitely relieved; (b) any slight hardening that may have developed in the plate adjacent to the weld zone as a result of a higher carbon content of plate material is relieved to some extent, permitting easier machining.

In order to have complete stress relief, it is necessary that the weldment be heated slowly and uniformly and cooled in a similar manner. The piece must be held at the maximum temperature sufficiently long for the heat to penetrate the heaviest members. Any departure from these standards simply means that the stresses are only partially relieved. Therefore, to ensure a complete heat-treatment, the furnace should be furnished with automatic temperature-recording equipment.

There is considerable question as to the necessity for stress-relieving many types of welded bases, and it must be granted that many of them are regularly manufactured without this treatment and give satisfactory service. One type of base that certainly requires stress relieving is the extra-heavy rigid type subjected to considerable external stress. Any residual stresses present in the frame members would nullify the effective resistance of the members to withstand the external stress by the amount of the residual stress. The bases of precision machinery should always be stress-relieved. Any machine elements that must be machined and held to close tolerances should be stress-relieved after fabrication. Light flexible weldments that are free to come and go should require no heat-treatment. Also, it should be unnecessary to stress-relieve weldments that merely support machinery and are not subject to any great stress.

Cleaning the Weldment

The weldment is scaled by the stress-relieving temperature and is cleaned up by either a motor-driven wire brush or by sandblasting. The wire brush will take off all loose scale and oxide and leave a suitable surface for painting. A portable grinder is used to remove weld reinforcement and spatter and to smooth corners and rough spots. It is customary to grind butt welds flush with the plate, and outside corner welds to a uniform radius. Sandblasting is more costly than wire-brushing, but it does a more thorough job and is frequently specified for cleaning the inside of oil and coolant reservoirs.

CHAPTER 8

Welding Processes

Shielded-Arc Process

The development of the shielded-arc electrode must be recorded as the outstanding achievement in arc welding since its inception. In most respects, shielded-arc weld metal is actually superior to the machinery steel upon which it is deposited in the fabrication of machine bases. This process has permitted the successful fabrication of many types of rigid and highly stressed structures that previously had been considered beyond the scope of welding.

If an arc is drawn between a bare electrode and a low-carbon-steel plate, the deposited metal is contaminated by the surrounding air and is badly oxidized and high in nitrogen content. The weld is consequently porous and rather low in resistance to impact, corrosion, and fatigue stresses.

Shielding prevents air contamination; hence there is very little oxidation and a low nitrogen content. The welds are high in strength and ductility and in resistance to impact, corrosion, and fatigue.

Table 8–1 shows the differences in chemical composition and physical properties of bare and shielded-arc deposited weld metal.

Methods of Shielding the Arc

There are three general methods used in shielding arc-fused steel: (1) by means of a heavy covering on the electrode, (2) by enclosing the arc in a gaseous shroud of reducing gases introduced from an external source, and (3) by fusing the rod under a blanket of protective slag.

TABLE 8–1

BARE-ELECTRODE AND SHIELDED-ARC WELD METAL*

Metal content and properties	Bare electrode	Shielded electrode
Carbon	0.02–0.06	0.08–0.13
Manganese	0.10–0.20	0.25–0.45
Silicon	0.05	0.05–0.10
Phosphorus	0.015–0.025	0.015–0.025
Sulphur	0.015–0.025	0.015–0.025
Oxide	0.25–0.35	0.05–0.07
Nitride	0.10–0.15	0.018–0.025
Ultimate strength, p.s.i.	45,000–55,000	60,000–75,000
Yield point, p.s.i.	Near breaking load	45,000–55,000
Per cent elongation in 2 in.	5–10	20–30
Reduction of area, per cent	Below 10	40–60
Density, grams per square centimeter	7.4–7.7	7.83–7.86
Izod, ft.-lb.	5–15	50–80
Fatigue, p.s.i.	11,000–16,000	26,000–33,000
Corrosion resistance	Poor	Better than mild-steel plate
X ray	Quite porous	Practically free of defects

* Both types of welds were made with an electrode of the following analysis:

Carbon.........0.10–0.14 per cent
Manganese......0.30–0.50 per cent
Silicon.........0.06 per cent maximum
Sulphur.........0.025 per cent maximum
Phosphorus......0.025 per cent maximum

(1) *Covered Electrode with Reducing Gas Predominating.* This type of shielded-arc electrode usually has an extruded covering consisting of cellulosic material with slag- and arc-stabilizing elements and metallic deoxidizers. This coating is secured by a suitable binder. Upon combustion, cellulose gives off carbon monoxide and hydrogen gases that surround the arc and protect the

deposited weld metal from air contamination. An electrode of this type depends almost entirely upon gaseous shielding action and causes formation of a minimum amount of residual slag. It is adapted for universal application (flat, vertical, and overhead) and has excellent penetration. The arc action of this type of electrode is illustrated in Fig. 8–1. Note that the electrode melts faster than

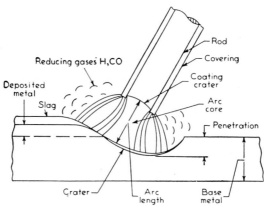

Fig. 8-1. Diagrammatic sketch of shielded arc.

the coating, forming an inverted crucible at the arc end that serves to protect the electrode tip from air contamination while it is melting from the arc heat.

(2) *Covered Electrode with Slag Protection Predominating.* This type of covering consists mainly of slag-forming ingredients with arc-stabilizing elements and metallic deoxidizers. The shielding action is mostly due to mechanical and chemical protection of the deposited steel pellets by the molten slag that surrounds the pellets as they are propelled across the arc. The slag then accumulates at the rear of the arc crater to form a complete covering over the deposited weld. The cellulose content is usually low and in some electrodes is entirely absent. The inverted crucible is essential as in Type 1. Electrodes of this type are termed "hot-spot" rods for heavy-duty flat welding of both grooves and fillets and are not so penetrative as Type 1 electrodes.

(3) *Covered Electrode with Gas-Slag Protection.* This type of shielded-arc electrode has a heavy extruded coating and depends upon both gas and slag protection. Some groove and fillet rods

are of this type and are also known as "hot-spot" rods. These are more penetrative than Type 2 but not so penetrative as Type 1.

(4) *Gaseous Shroud.* The atomic-hydrogen process and the inert-gas shielded-arc processes are examples of shielding by means of a gaseous shroud. In the former, the arc is drawn between bare tungsten electrodes; in the latter, between a tungsten electrode and the work. The operator feeds in a bare filler rod, and the shielding is accomplished entirely by the reducing blanket of gases which surround the weld and which are introduced from an external source.

(5) *Hidden-Arc Process.* The arc is drawn beneath a blanket of slag while a bare alloy electrode is fed into the arc. The deposited metal is protected from air contamination by the complete slag covering.

Electrode Composition

There are many different compositions of electrodes designed for welding different alloys, these compositions usually being similar to the alloy (parent metal) to be welded. Alloying ingredients are introduced in the coating as well as in the electrode.

For welding machinery steel, some mild-steel electrodes are universal in their scope, whereas others are limited in their application. One type is for heavy fillet work. Another type is for groove welding, and a third is designed for the finishing bead of a groove weld. There are still other variations such as coatings adapted for AC and DC welding, and for deep and shallow penetration.[1]

Methods of Welding Used in the Commercial Weldery

(1) *Manual Metallic Shielded Arc.* In this process, the operator uses a 14-in. or an 18-in. electrode gripped in an electrode holder so that all manipulation of the arc is manually controlled. The electrodes vary in diameter from $\frac{3}{32}$ to $\frac{3}{8}$ in. This process is almost universally used in fabricating machine bases, since there is either an insufficient number of a kind or because the general

---

[1] For detailed information on arc-welding techniques, the reader is referred to the following sources of information: (1) *A. W. S. Welding Handbook*, American Welding Society, New York, 1942; (2) *Procedure Handbook of Arc Welding Design and Practice*, 8th ed., The Lincoln Electric Company, Cleveland, 1945; (3) *The Welding Encyclopedia*, 11th ed., McGraw-Hill Book Company, Inc., 1943.

shape and nature of the work excludes automatic welding. Machine-base weldments are usually made up of many ribs and partitions of irregular shapes, and the seams are relatively short and varying in section. The manual operator can start quickly and change his position without great delay. He can also vary the amount of metal deposited at will and in many such cases can make better time than would be possible by automatic means. So we find that although automatic arc welding utilizes higher amperages and greater linear speeds than manual welding does, these advantages are lost if the arc drawing time is short and there are many different welding positions.

Manual welding may have either an AC or DC source of electricity. The amperage may run between 50 amp. for a $\frac{3}{32}$-in. electrode and 500 amp. for a $\frac{3}{8}$-in. electrode. Machine bases fabricated out of $\frac{1}{4}$-in. plate and heavier are usually arc-welded with $\frac{1}{4}$-in. electrodes using from 300 to 400 amp.

(2) *Automatic Metallic Arc Welding (Shielded and Unshielded).* In this type of welding, the electrode feed and the control of the arc length or the arc voltage are accomplished by means of a special automatic welding head. The operator handles switches that vary the amperage and arc voltage, and he has direct control of the electrode position in relation to the work. For a given adjustment, the welding head will feed the electrode into the arc at a uniform rate and will maintain a constant arc wattage. There are two positioning methods. In one, the welding head is mounted in a stationary position with the work rotated or moved in a linear direction. In the other, the work remains stationary while the welding head travels on a track parallel to the seam line. Both methods require a definite relationship between the seam line and the arc position within rather narrow limits, which the operator makes up by adjusting the electrode position as it is fed toward the work.

Automatic metallic arc welding was first used in the automotive industry for seam-welding rear-axle housings, drive shafts, muffler assemblies, torque tubes, shock absorbers, and wheel assemblies. In welding rear-axle housings of the banjo type, it has been customary to use two stampings that are half sections cut parallel to the center line of the axle. These stampings are clamped securely together in a fixture, and two welding heads mounted on an overhead track start at the inside ends of the seams to weld out simultaneously. The fixture is then revolved 180 deg. so that the other side may be welded. The operator must set up the work and remove the completed unit.

Automobile drive shafts usually consist of a seamless tube with premachined forgings pressed on at each end. The two forgings are circumferentially welded to the tubing by means of stationary heads mounted directly above the seam lines with a rotating type of fixture holding the assembly. The operator places the assembly in the fixture and presses a push button that starts the rotating mechanism and the electrode feed. An automatic cutoff switch breaks the current to stop the rotation and feed after the arc has completed its travel, usually after the arc has overlapped the starting point by about the length of the crater.

In the above processes, automatic operation exceeds manual operation because the assemblies are great in number and uniform in size and shape for a given production run. Consequently, a fixture can be built that will keep the arc and seam position constant. One operator can control two arcs, and a weld is made at a linear rate many times greater than the manual all-day welding rate. The welds, being machine-made, are more uniform in appearance, and the electrode stub-end loss of approximately 15 per cent, present in manual operation, is eliminated. Also, the shape of the bead can be controlled by positioning the electrode angle of feed with respect to the work. The bead contour will remain constant, and a flat or high bead can be developed in this manner.

The fabricators of cylindrical shapes, such as pipes, tanks, and boilers, were also among the first to use automatic welding extensively. In their work, the assembly is placed on rollers with the welding heads mounted on an overhead track. For the welding of circumferential seams, the heads remain stationary while the cylinder rotates. For longitudinal seams, the cylinder is stationary while the welding head traverses the length.

In regard to machinery applications, the weldery uses the automatic process with a rotating type of fixture for welding cylindrical shapes, or a tractor type of unit by which the welding unit is taken to the work or the work is taken to the welding unit. These types have been used extensively and should find many more applications in shops handling duplicate pieces of heavy machinery.

Figure 8–2 shows a stationary automatic type of welding head with the work revolved in a fixture.

COURTESY MCNEIL MACHINE AND ENGINEERING CO.

Fig. 8-2. Special rotating-type fixture for welding a large circular weldment (rear view) .

If a weldery is fabricating a group of 20 heavy weldments in which there are required four ½-in. outside fillet welds 6 ft. in length, it would be economical to weld these four heavy seams automatically with a tractor-type unit even though the remainder of the welding is best suited for manual operation. If the weldery is engaged in making these bases in steady production lots over a long period, it would be advisable to go a step further and make a permanent fixture for welding two or more seams at one time. Such a fixture would of course have a track mounting set properly relative to the seam line. Figure 8–3 shows the application of the automatic shielded-arc welding process in fabricating the frame of a metalworking band saw. The work is stationary and the motor driven welding head travels on an overhead beam. The hidden-arc

COURTESY LINCOLN ELECTRIC CO.

Fig. 8-3. Fabricating the frame of a metalworking band saw by means of the hidden-arc automatic welding process.

process is shown in welding a 78-in. butt seam in 10-gauge steel. In replacing manual welding with the automatic welding process, the time required to produce this weld was reduced from six minutes to one minute.

Figure 8–4 shows a fixture of the spinner type holding a large tire-vulcanizing machine bed in a position for a linear trough weld. The heavy horizontal lap seams are being welded by the tape shielding process. A gantry-crane mounting is used for the welding equipment and the operator. The work is stationary and the arc traverses the length of the seam.

(A) *Light-coated Automatic Unshielded Welding Wire.* Figure 8–5 shows an automatic head mounted on a small motor-driven tractor unit that carries a small coil of electrode and has the controls built in for operating the feed. In this particular instance, a light-coated high-speed unshielded welding wire is being used; at a given current, it will melt considerably faster than an ordinary

COURTESY MCNEIL MACHINE AND ENGINEERING CO.

Fig. 8-4. Fixture of the spinner-type mounting a large tire-vulcanizing machine bed.

bare wire. The higher speed is due partly to the electrode design and partly to the flux used.

Deeply dented wire, as shown in Fig. 8–6, is made by passing round wire through a set of indenting rolls. The four rows of indentations or dents thus obtained in the electrode surface are filled with a flux that promotes a high melting rate. This design permits a large amount of flux to be carried in the dents without impairing the electrical conductivity of the outer surface.

Other types of light-coated automatic welding electrodes are shown in Fig. 8–7. In all these methods of coating, the main objective is to apply a uniform coating of flux in sufficient quantity

Fig. 8-5. Automatic welding head for feeding light-coated wire from a coil. The head with controls is mounted on a light motor-driven tractor that travels adjacent to the seam line.

to promote a high melting rate and at the same time to retain the electrical conductivity of the electrode surface. These light-coated electrodes were used in the first automatic arc-welding installations. Even though the weld was unshielded, they possessed excellent speed characteristics and gave good results. Rods of this type are still used where welds of extremely high quality are not required.

(B) *The Shielded Automatic Process.* Following the development of the manual shielded-arc process of metallic arc welding, it was only natural that automatic shielded-arc processes would follow. All manual shielded-arc electrodes have relatively heavy coatings that are nonconductive. For automatic shielded arc welding, the problem is to feed the electrode in continuous or long lengths and to establish electrical contact near the arc end so that a high amperage may be carried through the electrode without overheating.

Figure 8–8 shows a process for feeding bare rod into the automatic head and introducing a tape impregnated with flux ingredients just below the point of electrical brush contact. Here, light-coated welding wire is fed from a coil. A short distance in

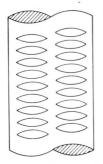

Fig. 8-6. Flux-dented electrode.

advance of the arc, a shielding type of tape is wrapped around the wire by means of forming rolls, which are mounted in a housing directly below the welding head. The tape consists of cellulose impregnated with ingredients usually found in a manual rod of similar type. The ratio of flux to steel is also similar to that in the manual rod of similar type. The process permits current contact near the arc end and the introduction of a heavy type of coating. In all such developments, the designer attempts to reduce the distance between the brush contact and the arc end to a minimum. The flux tape is wrapped around the wire by means of grooved wheels. Once set, the tape retains this form.

By another method, the wire is in coil form and coated with a cotton braid impregnated with flux ingredients. Electrical contact is established by milling a groove in the coating parallel with the axis of the wire, after which sliding brush contact is made in the slot.

In a third process, used originally by some pressure-vessel manufacturers, the covered electrode is manufactured in long straight lengths, and current-contact tabs are welded on at frequent intervals. The current contact is transferred from one tab to the next as the rod melts down.

In a fourth process, the bare rod is covered with a woven mesh of wire or is wrapped spirally with a wire having a composition similar to the base rod. Flux is applied between the outer wire strands, the outside surface of the strands being left bare for electrical contact. This fabricated wire is processed and baked and is supplied in coil form.

(C) *The Automatic Hidden-Arc Process.* A shielded automatic method of welding known as the "hidden-arc process" has advanced rapidly in recent years. Its results have been so successful that the process ranks as an outstanding achievement in welding. Previous methods of automatic arc welding used a maximum current of

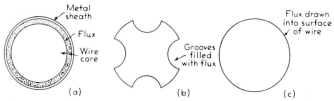

Fig. 8-7. Light coated automatic wire. (a) metal-sheath covered; (b) grooved wire; (c) composite type.

about 600 amp. With the hidden-arc method, the current range has been extended to 4000 amp. with a proportional increase in the melting rate of the electrode.

Figure 8–9 shows a sketch of the process as it is applied in making a vee butt weld between heavy plate members. An automatic welding head is used to feed the electrode, which is a coil of bare rod of special alloy analysis. By using a bare wire, the difficulty of establishing good electrical contact near the arc end is avoided. The melt, consisting of a special slag pulverized to fairly uniform size, is fed through a melt-feed tube in advance of the electrode, and the arc is established by inserting a piece of steel wool between the rod and the work. After the arc is established, the electrode is fed down and advanced at the same time to complete the seam.

The heat developed in the hidden-arc method of welding is so intense that it penetrates rapidly and widens out to create a bead of considerable volume. Because of this high penetrative power, it is not necessary to vee out to the bottom of a plate as for single groove welds by other methods. The small welding vee is shown in Fig. 8–9. The bead of weld metal consists of about 2 parts of plate metal to 1 part of filler metal. The melting action of the process takes place entirely under the slag, so that the operator sees no evidence of either an arc or a welding flame; consequently, he needs no protective shield.

Because of the intensity of the heat penetration, it is necessary to have good fits and to back up the bottom of vee welds to

Fig. 8-8. Automatic shielded arc-welding unit, flux-tape method, with tractor mounting.

prevent burn-throughs. The backing is a copper bar or the slag itself, held in place by a pneumatic slag-supporting device. The welds are frequently made in a single pass even on heavy plate

sections. Although the grain is rather coarse, it must be emphasized
that the welds are of the highest quality, having unusual strength,
ductility, shock resistance, with uniform density, low nitrogen
content, and excellent corrosion resistance, and thus are generally
equal to the best obtained by manual shielded-arc welding methods.
The process is applicable to laps, fillets, butts, grooves, and plug
welds. Because of the high amperage and great fluidity developed,
it is necessary to weld in a nearly horizontal plane, though the
process is applied to circumferential seams of rather small diameter.
Light-gauge welds have been made at the rate of more than 100 in.
per minute. Single-pass vee welds are made in 2½-in. plate using

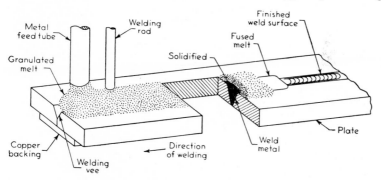

Fig. 8-9. Diagrammatic sketch of the hidden-arc process.

a ½-in. electrode at 4000 amp. at the rate of 3 in. per minute.
Fillet welds with ⅜-in. legs can be made without troughing.

The hidden-arc process is illustrated photographically in Fig.
8–10, which shows the pile of flux deposited from the flux box.
A bare-alloy electrode is fed into the arc from a coil by means of
an automatic welding head. A substantial amount of flux is fed
to the seam line immediately in advance of the arc. The flux
hopper and flux tube are shown attached to the welding head
The arc occurs underneath the blanket of slag. Note the small
percentage of flux that is actually fused. When cooled, the unfused
flux to the right of the solid slag is returned to the hopper for
further use. This method of welding was largely responsible for the
high speed obtained in welding plate assemblies for ships during
World War II.

(3) *Automatic Shielded Carbon-Arc Process.* In this method,

the arc is drawn between the work and a carbon electrode; hence the arc may traverse the seam with no addition of filler metal. For example, an edge weld of two flanged sections can be made by merely melting down the edges without additional electrode feed. It is also possible to make a full-section butt weld in light members by a single pass without electrode addition. In making fillet welds or in any cases where additional metal is required, a separate electrode feed is used. Shielding of the carbon arc is

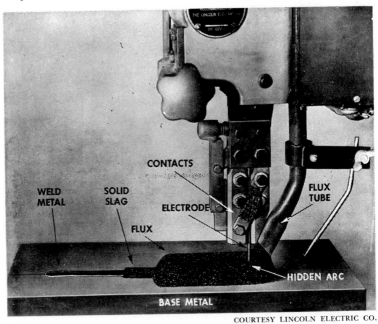

Fig. 8-10. Hidden-arc welding process. The wire is fed from a coil.

accomplished by introducing an organic substance into the arc in the form of a fibrous material, a powder, or a paste. The combustion of the organic substance bathes the arc in carbon monoxide and hydrogen gases and protects the weld metal from oxidation. In general, this process has the same uses and limitations as automatic shielded metallic arc welding, described in Section 2, above.

(4) *Manual Oxyacetylene Gas Welding.* Gas seam welding has little application in the weldery engaged in heavy machine-base

fabrication, since it is less economical for heavy members than the electric-arc method. The process is used extensively in welderies engaged in the fabrication of sheet metal below 16 gauge. The oxyacetylene torch is also used for brazing copper or brass screens and malleable pipe fittings. The parent metal is heated to about 1600° F., a temperature that does not melt the surfaces but does permit a good bond to form between the parent metal and the bronze filler metal. A flux is required to keep the surfaces clean.

The gas welding torch is used extensively in plate straightening. When the flame is applied to a small area in a plate, the metal there tends to expand but is restricted by the cold adjacent metal. This heated metal is locally upset upon cooling, and the contraction is permanent, thereby providing a method of removing warps, bulges, or bends in structural sections or plates. To remove a bulge from a plate surface, the flame is directed at the high (convex) side of the bulge. The same procedure is used in straightening welded units or in correcting bent and distorted pieces.

(5) *Automatic Oxyactylene Flame Welding.* This process is used for welding light-walled tubing by continuous rolling. The machine takes bar strip in coils and forms it into tubing that is accurately sized in a train of rolls. The seam is at the top and passes under a series of oxyacetylene flames that quickly raise the temperature of the joint to the fusion point. The tubing is then cut off to size. The rate of travel is high because of the use of multiple flames in tandem, and the quality of the weld is excellent because of the nonoxidizing nature of the oxyacetylene flame. Flame welding is applicable for plain cold-rolled or hot-rolled steels, stainless steel, and a wide variety of alloy steels. Eighteen-gauge material can be welded at speeds up to 150 ft. per minute.

(6) *Atomic Hydrogen Welding (Manual and Automatic).* In this method of arc welding, the arc is drawn between tungsten electrodes and is shielded by hydrogen gas fed from a portable tank. The degree of shielding is high, and welds of extra-fine quality are readily obtained. The weld is dense, smooth, and of good appearance, being almost entirely free of scale on the surface. The high efficiency of the shielding medium plus the preheating quality of the flame makes this process useful with alloy metals that are difficult to weld by other methods. The process has been used particularly for repairing or altering dies, for applying hard-surfacing

overlays, and for fabricating light-gauge mild-steel and stainless-steel sheets. It is used in either manual or automatic operation.

(7) *Inert Gas-shielded Arc Welding.* This method involves a combination of gas and arc similar to the atomic hydrogen process. Here, however, the arc is drawn directly between a tungsten electrode and the work instead of between two tungsten electrodes; helium or argon gas is used instead of hydrogen gas. Argon is generally preferred, since it is readily obtainable commercially in a high degree of purity, an essential factor in producing high-quality welds, and is less expensive than helium.

A special welding torch holds the tungsten electrode. A water cooling system circulates through the head of the torch, thereby permitting higher welding currents. The current conductor enters through the outlet tube. There is also a gas inlet leading to the mixing chamber. Despite these many passages, the torch is light, compact, and easily manipulated.

The three sources of welding current in order of preference are as follows: alternating, direct with negative electrode, and direct with positive electrode. This preference is based on the amount of current used, the limiting factor being the amount of heat developed in the electrode, which is at a minimum for alternating current and at a maximum for direct positive current. In order to utilize an AC source, it is necessary to superimpose a high-frequency current to facilitate starting the arc at low amperages. Also, this high-frequency current permits longer arcs and greater arc stability.

Inert gas-shielded arc welding, which is of fairly recent origin, came forward during World War II in the welding of magnesium and aluminum alloys and stainless steels. Although these three fields represent the major uses in a quantitative sense, the process is also applied to such hard-to-weld metals as monel, brass, Inconel, and pure silver. It can be used for hard-surfacing and for brazing silver and silver alloys upon steel. No flux is required in any of these welds.

The broadest application of the process is in the fabrication of aluminum and its alloys. Commonly welded nonheat-treatable alloys are 2S, 3S, and 52S. Heat-treatable alloys welded are 24S, 53S, and 61S. The process has been used on plates up to $5/8$-in. thickness with a maximum amperage of 800. It has been used on stainless steel types 302, 304, 316, 327, 347, and 410.

With the currently increased production of aluminum and magnesium alloys, it is probable that these metals will find considerable use for machine frames where minimum weight is a requisite.

Poke Welding

Poke welding is similar to plug welding. The process is used in lining steel plate with thin sheets of stainless steel or other alloys. Holes are punched or drilled, and the welds resemble resistance spot welding. The poke-welding process takes more time but is flexible in its application.

Resistance Welding

This method has only a limited application in the fabrication of heavy machine bases, since the heavy plates and rolled steel sections are frequently covered with rust and scale and can be more readily welded by the electric arc. Furthermore, fillets and butt seams of varying length and position are required, further limiting the resistance process. For the fabrication of light machine bases, the resistance process has many applications. Cold-rolled or pickled sheets are free of oxide and are generally recommended.

There are three main types of resistance welds in common use, plus three variations.

(1) *Spot Welding.* This is usually a lap weld and is made by contacting the opposite faces of the sheets with heavy electrodes. A high current is passed at low voltage, and pressure is applied to complete the weld.

(2) *Seam Welding.* A continuous or intermittent weld is made by roller contacts and pressure. The usual form of the weld is either lap or butt.

(3) *Butt Weld.* The parts to be joined carry the current and are brought together under great pressure as a heavy current is passed. There is a considerable upset at the junction.

(4) *Flash Welding.* This is the simplest method of joining two bars, pieces of tubing, or rod end to end. The two ends to be welded are held in jaws opposite each other and act as electrodes (see Fig. 8–11). When the current arcs across the gap separating the two ends, the facing metal quickly heats up, and bits of metal begin to flash back and forth. At the instant the power is cut off,

the two ends are mechanically forced together and will cool in a fused condition.

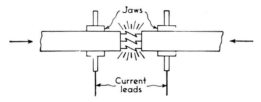

Fig. 8-11. Flash weld.

(5) *Projection Welding.* Projection welding is a form of spot welding, except that small projections on one or more members localize the heat and promote the weld.

(6) *Percussion Welding.* These welds are characterized by the facts that a supply of direct current is essential, that there is a sudden discharge of electrical energy at the junction with an arc which is extinguished by a percussive blow, and that the united surfaces are partially fluid.

Thermit Welding

This method, used in both the manufacture and repair of heavy machinery, is the most economical for creating welds of great volume. Thermit welding is really a casting process. The ends to be welded are first sandblasted clean and separated. A wax pattern is then developed where the weld is to be made. A sand mold is fitted in place, and the wax is melted by means of a blowtorch, so that a cavity is left for the weld. The ends to be welded are usually preheated. The thermit mixture consists of iron oxide (ferrosoferric oxide, Fe_3O_4) and finely divided aluminum powder. The mixture is ignited in a crucible by means of magnesium. The reaction evolves heat and is quite rapid, producing pure iron and Al_2O_3 slag. The iron is tapped into the mold and a weld is made as in the steel foundry. It is possible to melt down alloys of many analyses. The quality of the weld is excellent.

Forge Welding

The blacksmith or forge weld is the oldest welding process. It consists of heating the parts that are to be united to a plastic stage. Sand or other suitable flux is then sprinkled along the surfaces where the weld is to be made in order to dissolve the iron oxide. The parts are then superimposed and united by rapid hammer blows. This process has very limited application in the fabrication of machine bases.

Furnace Brazing

Furnace brazing consists of copper-brazing an assembly of steel parts. Copper wire is placed at each joint, and the assembly is furnace-heated in a hydrogen atmosphere to about 2100° F., causing the copper wire to melt and flow into the joints by capillary action. The hydrogen atmosphere is beneficial in preventing the formation of oxides on the steel surface. Clean surfaces are required in making a copper-to-steel weld.

Crosley Motors, Inc., has used the furnace brazing process for welding up its cylinder block, which consists entirely of small steel stampings. Assemblies are passed through the furnace on a conveyor. At the front end of the furnace the temperature is set for brazing, and at the rear the temperature is lowered to heat-treat certain metal parts. This process is quite applicable to small machine bases made of steel stampings.

CHAPTER 9

Flame Cutting and Flame Hardening

EVER SINCE the earliest use of arc welding for fabricating machinery frames and parts, the engineer has recognized the oxyacetylene flame-cutting process as a vital tool in this field. The modern process of fabricating machine bases would be impractical without this simple method of shaping steel.

Ordinary hot-rolled low-carbon steel plates, such as boiler plates and machinery steel, from light gauge up to 24 in. or more in thickness, are readily cut to any desired shape or pattern with a maximum variation of $\frac{3}{16}$ in. Furthermore, these low-carbon steels (0.30 per cent carbon or less) are flame-cut without any appreciable degree of hardening along their cut edges, so that the cuts can generally be made without preheating or postheating.

Description of Flame-Cutting Process

Briefly, the oxyacetylene flame-cutting process consists of pre-heating a small spot on the subject metal with an oxyacetylene flame to the kindling point (about 1600° F. for steel) and then impinging upon it a jet of pure oxygen that causes the steel to oxidize or burn rapidly. The operator then advances the cutting flame at a rate that will permit a complete cut through the plate. Only iron and metals of high iron content can be cut with the oxyacetylene torch. The chemical reaction is

$$3Fe + 2O_2 = F_3O_4$$

This reaction evolves a considerable amount of heat. Theoretically, 4.6 cu. ft. of oxygen will oxidize 1 lb. of iron to FeO. The heat of combustion of 1 lb. of iron is 2900 B.t.u. The torch is designed in such a way that the preheating flame surrounding the oxygen jet will preheat ahead of the cut and raise it to the kindling point. There are many variations of the cutting torch for specialized uses, but all mix the oxygen and acetylene gases in the proper proportion for preheating and then introduce the oxygen jet for cutting.

Fuel Gases

A number of different fuel gases have been substituted for acetylene. Although some of them cost less than acetylene, the fact that they generally require considerably more oxygen nullifies their cost advantage. Acetylene is preferred for preheating, since it yields the highest flame temperature (about 6000° F.) and permits a more rapid rate of preheating. It is also a safe gas to handle and is available commercially.

Table 9–1 shows the corresponding oxygen and fuel-gas consumptions for four common types of fuel gases. These comparisons were made on the basis of similar cutting performance.

TABLE 9–1

FUEL-GAS AND OXYGEN CONSUMPTION

Fuel gas	Volume of fuel gas, cu. ft. per hr.	Volume of oxygen, cu. ft. per hr.
Acetylene................	10	17
City (manufactured) gas.....	75	56
Natural gas..............	28	56
Propane.................	10	45

Tables are available for all types of flame-cutting equipment showing the proper oxygen and acetylene or other fuel-gas pressures, the correct nozzle size for the thickness of plate to be cut, and the correct cutting speed.

Preheating

The preheating temperature will vary between 200 and 1000° F., depending upon the composition and size of the plate being cut. The usual preheating temperature is between 500 and 600° F. The preheating temperature should be low as possible, to avoid injury to the steel; and cutting should follow immediately, once the correct temperature is reached. It is important to avoid large differences in temperature between the outside surface and the interior of the subject metal, since they upset the uniformity of cutting. A difference of only 100° F. is sufficient to ruin the cut. An asbestos-paper covering is frequently used to confine the heat to the subject metal.

Methods of Flame Cutting

There are three types of cutting in general use: manual operation, semiautomatic, and full automatic.

In the manual process, the operator holds the torch and controls its movements manually.

COURTESY REPUBLIC STRUCTURAL IRON WORKS.

Fig. 9-1. Multiple-torch unit employing a template made of ¼- x ⅜-in. aluminum strip mounted on 12-gauge sheet metal.

In the semiautomatic method, the torch is attached to a flame-cutting machine that operates on the pantograph principle. The template is traced by manual operation. One type of tracer is a wheel that follows the straight lines automatically and must be guided around corners and curves. The other type is a knurled spindle that must be manually guided about a masonite template.

If there are many duplicate parts, a special track template is prepared of either plastic or aluminum strip on which the follower wheel travels automatically to produce identical cuts, two or more

COURTESY REPUBLIC STRUCTURAL IRON WORKS.

Fig. 9-2. With the magnetic tracer, a steel template may be placed anywhere on table, and the cutout is followed automatically.

torches being attached to the machine to increase the production rate (Fig. 9–1). The magnetic tracer automatically follows the inside or the outside form of the template made of $5/16$-in. or $3/8$-in. plate. In common use, the magnetic tracer is quite accurate (Fig. 9–2).

The Electric-Eye Tracer

An electric-eye tracing device for pantograph-type oxyacetylene machines has come into use recently. This process completely eliminates expensive metal and wood templates and all other mechanical or manual auxiliary guiding devices. The electronically controlled tracing equipment will cut complicated shapes with great precision from simple outline drawings or silhouettes. There are no limitations to the variety of designs which may be cut, since the electronic tracing head follows complex angles and curves with extreme accuracy.

A new field of application has been opened in machine production flame cutting through the "chain" method of reproduction made possible with the electric eye. In the chain method, a series of identical shapes are drawn on the template and connected with a continuous line, making production cutting of several pieces possible in a single operation.

Tolerance in Flame-cutting Operations

The tolerances in manual cutting operations are mostly dependent upon the operator. In the fabrication of large machinery frames, many cuts must be made manually. A good operator using a straightedge or guide can make a straight-line cut almost as accurately as an automatic cutting machine. In making irregular cuts, the operator follows a full-scale drawing inscribed upon the plate in chalk.

The accuracy of machine automatic cutting will depend upon the alignment of the machinery, the accuracy with which the metal is removed from the cut, and the degree of plate distortion resulting from heat absorbed in the cutting process. In normal cutting operations on $\frac{1}{4}$-in. to 6-in. plate, it is not difficult to meet tolerances of $\pm \frac{1}{16}$ in. On similar work for which a track template is used, a tolerance of $\pm \frac{1}{32}$ in. is possible if considerable care is taken.

Distortion of Plates $\frac{1}{2}$ In. Thick and Greater

When heat is applied to a plate edge, as produced in cutting, the plate heats up and tends to take on a convex shape. Distortion is not serious on long straight cuts unless the cutoff is very narrow. A large complicated shape involving inside cutting also presents a problem.

Inside cutting is the cutting out of metal from a plate, leaving the outer plate edge intact. When cuts are made into the outside edge of the plate, they are known as profile or outside cuts.

The usual procedure is to make the inside cuts first. With equal heat distribution around these cuts, there is little distortion. The main profile cuts are then made, with skips left at the center and both ends. A skip is a short uncut section about an inch long which ties the cut-off portion to the main plate during the cooling period to prevent distortion. Skips are removed after the work has cooled.

The distortion in long parallel cuts has been overcome entirely by making the two cuts simultaneously, so that the heat input and the tendency to distort on one side counterbalances those on the other. In making long cutouts in heavy plate that is heated before cutting, it is necessary to make correction factors to compensate for the expansion and to determine them experimentally. Inside cutting complicates this problem.

Stack Cutting

In cutting a large number of duplicate pieces from relatively light material, the fabricator uses stack cutting, which materially

COURTESY REPUBLIC STRUCTURAL IRON WORKS.

Fig. 9-3. Sixteen pieces of 3/16.-in. plates for electric motor parts are being stack-cut.

reduces the cost of cutting as compared to individual cuts. In this process, the plates are sheared to a uniform size, stacked in a pile 3 to 4 in. thick, and then pressed tightly together in a press brake.

Tack welds are applied at intervals of about 5 in. to maintain the compression, and the stack is flame-cut as a single piece of steel. In this way, a large number of pieces may be cut true to size and of exceptionally smooth outline. Thin sheet, $\frac{1}{8}$ in. thick or less, warps and is rough-edged if cut singly. It is simple to separate the stack after completion of the cut.

Stack cutting is used on plates up to $\frac{1}{2}$ in. thick and is often preferred to die stamping when the quantities are insufficient to warrant a die charge. As an example of stack cutting, one shop regularly cuts six stacks of six $\frac{1}{4}$-in. plates simultaneously with a machine carrying six torches, producing 36 identical parts in one traverse of the template. Records show that in a period of 15 hr. and 50 min., including setup and cutting time, a total of 2724 pieces were cut at the rate of 172 pieces per hour (Fig. 9–3).

The plates used in stack cutting must be flat and free of heavy mill scale, rust, and paint. A space of only 0.003 in. between plates is sufficient to interrupt the cut. C-clamps are sometimes used for holding the plates together, but tack welding by the method described is superior. The same tolerances hold for a stack as for a single plate of the same thickness as the stack.

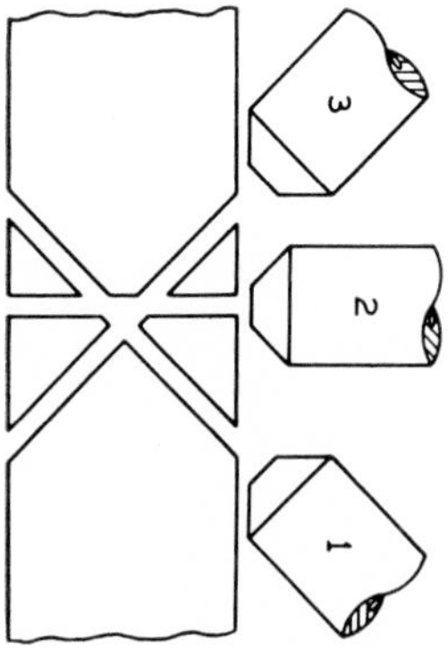

The Flame Planer

Multiface cutting, a new application of torch beveling, is used extensively in preparing heavy plates for single or double vee welding, since machining operations are slow and costly and single-torch cutting is slow and erratic. In double beveling it is important to hold the same relationship in angles, nose, and bevels throughout the length of the cut. The multiface cutting machine fulfills these

Fig. 9-4. Multiple cutting of double bevels with nose.

requirements. The three torches are securely clamped in a chosen relationship, and the group floats with the plate in traversing the length of the cut, so that the correct relationship is maintained irrespective of waves in the plate. The torch arrangement is illustrated in Fig. 9–4.

When a great number of accurate cuts must be made, it is the usual practice to proceed as shown in Fig. 9–5. The slab of steel is placed on the cutting table in contact with two stop blocks.

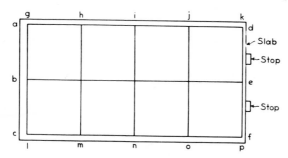

Fig. 9-5. Multiface cutting of double bevels with nose.

Multiple torches rigidly mounted on a traveling bridge make cuts *gl, hm, in, jo,* and *kp.* Another traveling bridge with multiple torches then produces cuts *ad, be,* and *cf.*

Flame Gouging

A special torch is available for cutting a groove or furrow ¾ to 4 in. wide on either a round or a flat surface. The torch is held tangent to the line of cut. The depth rarely exceeds ½ in. for a single pass. Flame gouging is used for burning out defective welds, preparing grooves for U-groove welding, removing surface defects in plates and castings, and removing metal from a round rotating piece in a lathe. The rate of metal removal is as high as 1800 lb. per hour, greatly in excess of the performance of a high-speed lathe used for a similar task.

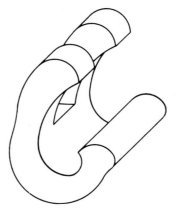

Fig. 9-6. Two-plane cutting.

Two-Plane Cutting

Flame cutting in two directions is used in creating complicated shapes that would be expensive to machine or forge. An example of the process is shown in Fig. 9–6.

Additional Applications of Flame Cutting

A large percentage of cutting operations takes place in ware-houses, steel mills, and fabricating shops in which the material is mostly low-carbon hot-rolled steel. The low-alloy high-strength steels are also cut for fabrication. For this work, the steel mill and warehouse use the tractor-type mounting by which the torch is

COURTESY REPUBLIC STRUCTURAL IRON WORKS.

Fig. 9-7. Taking ¾-in. excess from two 6-in. x 6-in. x 14-ft. forged bars tack-welded and clamped together to eliminate distortion.

mounted on a traveling carriage and follows a small track to make long straight cuts in heavy plate (Fig. 9–7). There are special cutting machines designed to cut circles, squares, and other definite shapes.

Effect of Flame Cutting on Steel

In the flame-cutting process, a kerf, or slit, of uniform width is burned through the plate. The steel immediately adjacent to the kerf is raised above the critical temperature and then rapidly chilled down through the critical range. In heavy plate, this cool-ing action is in the nature of a drastic quench. This zone is altered by the heat-treatment of the operation, but in steels with a carbon content well under 0.35 per cent, and cut at room temperature for machinery bases, the structure is largely sorbitic, or nearly pearlitic, and has properties of toughness and strength exceeding those of the original hot-rolled steel plate. The hardness is increased slightly, depending on the thickness of the plate. The depth of the altered zone also depends on the thickness of the material and is approximately as follows:

Plate Thickness, Inches	Depth Affected by Flame Cutting, Inches
$\frac{1}{2}$	$\frac{1}{32}$
6	$\frac{1}{8}$
30	$\frac{3}{8}$

When plate is beveled by flame cutting and an arc weld is made, the penetration of the weld will entirely obliterate the slight oxide scale along the edge of the kerf and the altered zone adjacent to the kerf. The deposition of multiple-layer welding will result in grain refinement of this zone and an annealing treatment that will completely obliterate the altered structure and replace it with a greatly improved grain structure.

The Boiler Code permits the use of flame-cut bevels on plate in which the carbon content does not exceed 0.35 per cent. The rules state further that gas-cut plate edges must be uniform and smooth, and that all loose scale and slag accumulations must be removed before welding. The discoloration of the cut edge is not considered to be detrimental oxidation.

Machinability of Flame-cut Edges

The oxyacetylene cut edge is readily machinable in the general class of low-carbon steels of 0.30 per cent maximum carbon and the low-alloy high-strength steels. Steels of medium and high carbon content require annealing or normalizing to improve machinability.

Metals and Alloys Suitable for Flame Cutting

Flame cutting is used for cutting low-, medium-, and high-carbon steels and a wide range of alloys such as manganese, nickel, and stainless steels. Plain carbon steels up to 0.35 per cent carbon may be cut cold without any preheating or postheating, as also can alloys having low to medium carbon content, such as the nickel steels and the nickel-chrome, nickel-molybdenum, chrome-vanadium, and low-tungsten steels.

Most higher alloys require preheating. Steels that harden when quenched from above the critical range require postheating. Air-hardening steels must be either cooled slowly or annealed after cutting, even though preheated.

Some alloys require, in addition to preheating, the application of heat during the entire cutting process, in order to avoid shrinkage cracks. The alloys in this classification are as follows: high-carbon steel, irrespective of alloy content; high-manganese and high-silicon steels; high-carbon nickel steel; most chrome; nickel steels; medium-carbon molybdenum steel; straight chrome steels, including the 4–6 per cent type; and chrome vanadium of the high-carbon type.

Some steels are hard to cut. In this group are high-speed steel and high-nickel stainless steel having 12 to 20 per cent chrome and 7 to 10 per cent nickel.

Cast iron is also cut with difficulty and requires a special procedure by which a reciprocating movement of the torch is necessary to wash out the slag. A wide jagged cut is produced.

Steel castings and forgings may also be flame-cut within the composition limits of the steels listed above.

Oxyacetylene Flame Hardening

Flame hardening is almost as old as flame cutting, though it has only recently been improved to the point where it has received wide usage. Hardening with the oxyacetylene flame consists in heating the wearing surfaces of a machine part above the critical temperature by means of the flame and then cooling with a suitable quenching agent, usually water or compressed air. The depth of the hardened zone varies from $\frac{1}{8}$ to $\frac{1}{4}$ in. and compares favorably with the casehardening process. The hardness can be tempered, as is done in furnace practice, by a second heating, with the depth of the flame-hardened zone being accurately controlled.

Plain carbon steels above 0.35 per cent carbon are readily hardened. The standard S.A.E. low-alloy steels containing manganese, chromium, nickel, and silicon, in concentrations from 0.50 to 2.0 per cent, can be appreciably hardened with a carbon

Fig. 9-8. Samples of flame-cut or sheared parts.

Fig. 98. (Cont.) Samples of flame-cut or sheared parts.

Fig. 9-8 (Cont.) Samples of flame-cut or sheared parts.

content as low as 0.25 per cent. Increasing the carbon content favors the hardness obtainable. Rail steel (0.80 per cent carbon) can be flame-hardened up to 450 Brinell by using a very mild quenching, and up to 700 Brinell with a rapid quenching. The S.A.E. low-alloy steels with carbon at 0.35 per cent can be hardened to 500 Brinell by using a moderate quenching. Certain semisteels and alloy cast irons common to machine-base construction are flame-hardened to increase the wearing resistance. The flame-hardened area (usually the slideway) is then ground to a finish. S.A.E. 1045 steel is commonly flame-hardened when used in the manufacture of gears, cams, slides, ball races, and similar tough parts.

Conclusion

Plates flame-cut to template are in many instances preferred to castings, stampings, and forgings when used for such machine parts as frames, frame sections, cams, gear blanks, levers, links, rings, hinges, dies, and heavy-walled cylinders. When the quantities are small, it will usually be found more economical to flame-cut than to form by any other method. Forging operations are slow and costly and frequently require expensive dies. The die cost for stampings is also great. It can be fairly stated that any shape which can be cut out of a plate can be produced more cheaply by flame cutting than by any other method, irrespective of the quantity and thickness of material, except for items within the limits for blanking and stamping when the quantities are so great that the die cost has little effect upon the unit cost.

Figure 9–8 (pages 137–139) shows designs actually produced by plate flame cutting. No dimensions are given, since the purpose is to illustrate the amazing variety of shapes that can be readily developed by flame cutting. As previously stated, the plate thickness may well be from 16 gauge to 10 in. or more, and the over-all dimensions may vary between a few inches and 20 ft. or more.

CHAPTER 10

Forming of Metals

Selection of Metal-forming Process

The broad subject of the forming of metals encompasses many processes with which the designer should be familiar, since they each have a distinct place in the economic development of machine bases. Moreover, some that are in limited use today may find much greater use as fabrication of machinery weldments continues to gain in scope.

The designer's choice of components in creating weldment designs is based upon one or more of the following factors:

(1) Thickness, size, and shape of the piece
(2) Physical requirements
(3) Number of duplicate pieces
(4) Tolerance limits
(5) Weldability
(6) Cost

The first consideration in the selection of a forming method is the thickness of the piece. Steel plates are uniform in thickness, and therefore any forms shaped out of plate in the press brake or by die stamping will have sections of uniform thickness. If the part requires a variation in thickness, the designer immediately thinks in terms of casting, die casting, or forging. A part that varies in both shape and thickness is in the same category.

The over-all dimensions also receive early consideration. Die work is expensive and requires much power. The largest stampings are light sheet metal for automobile and aircraft use where the desired quantities are great and the die expense is spread thin over

COURTESY E. W. BLISS CO.

Fig. 10-1. Large toggle press forms automobile roof. The machine is of the double-action toggle type of 900 tons capacity.

many parts (Fig. 10–1). If a similar shape is required in small quantities, it is necessary to form it in the press brake for which the cost per piece is much greater than for the stamping made in quantity lots (Fig. 10–2). The press-brake method is a more laborious means for closely approximating the work created in the

die-stamping press without the use of expensive dies. In order to create certain shapes, the fabricator must split the design and add flame cutting and welding to the bending operation. The scope of operations is greatly extended into the field of heavy plate, since the press brake does not require much power to put a single bend in a plate, in contrast to the power required by a die press to form a large stamping of irregular outline by one impression of the ram. The scope of the press brake is extended by bending hot.

COURTESY CLEVELAND CRANE AND ENGINEERING CO.

Fig. 10-2. Forming a wide U with curved bottom and curved corners in the brake.

The physical properties required in the machine part may be the deciding factor in the selection of a particular component. Take, for example, the crankshaft and connecting rods of the modern heavy-duty truck engine. The designer turns to the forging and alloy casting, which have the high torsional and shock resistance necessary for this type of automotive service. These processes are also suitable for forming the irregular shapes of these two elements—an important consideration. If the component is a gear blank, it can be made by several methods such as flame cutting from medium carbon or alloy steel, casting in steel or gray iron (plain or alloy), or by forging. The nature of the service, the

number of parts required, and the cost are the determining factors. Many machine-tool builders insist upon forgings for all their small gears because of the superior toughness of the material.

The number of duplicate parts must be considered in relation to the cost of stamping, forging, and casting. The die cost is high for die-stamping and forging, and the pattern expense is great for casting unless spread over many parts. For instance, it might prove to be good economy to use the press brake on a particular section up to a certain number of pieces, beyond which it would be cheaper to die-stamp the part. Shearing is the most economical method of producing either rectangular or circular plate sections. However, four shearing operations are required in forming a rectangular piece to exact size, whereas a single blanking operation is required with a power press. The designer should remember this difference when considering the quantities and the die cost.

The over-all tolerance permitted in producing a component is another factor in selecting the method of metal forming. If the component is small and is to be manufactured in large quantities to fairly exact dimensions with small tolerances, the designer considers the stamping, the forging, the die casting, and the precision casting. Further elimination will probably follow after the shape and physical properties of the element are considered.

Cost is the final consideration unless certain physical or shape requirements dictate the method. The designer must consider not only the cost of the element itself but also the cost of the element with respect to the cost of the entire weldment. It is possible that the use of a stamping, forging, or some other precision component in a weldment may eliminate costly bending or machining operations that would make up the extra cost in preparing the precision part.

In design work related to machine-base weldments, many types of components may be used, of which the most essential, the cut shape, has been described at length in Chapter 9. The other components will be described in this chapter. Processes for preparing the other components are listed below in the order of their importance to the commercial weldery:

(1) Bending
(2) Cold-rolling

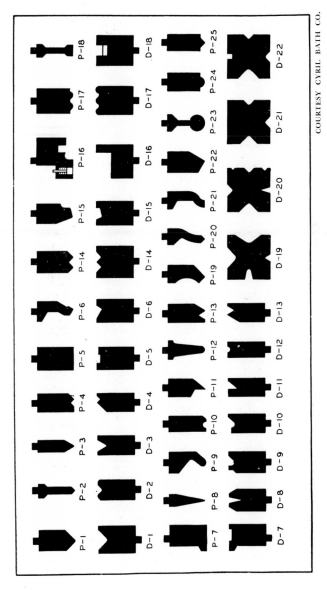

Fig. 10-3. Some of the many die shapes available for press-brake work.

(3) Flanging and dishing
(4) Tangent bending and contour forming
(5) Forging
(6) Steel casting
(7) Die stamping
(8) Die casting
(9) Plastic molding

Plate Forming by the Press Brake

The press brake is a fairly recent tool that has come into general adoption along with the increased use of steel plate and the process of fabrication by welding. In some production shops, the presses are equipped with a standard dieset to do a definite bending operation on a continuous production schedule. The commercial weldery uses one or more brakes to perform a wide variety of bending operations on many types of metals of varying thickness and size. Because of the wide scope of the work, the weldery has a large assortment of dies which suffice for almost any bending operation (Fig. 10–3).

The majority of bends made in machine-base work are 90 deg., though the press brake can develop bends of many angles, using the same die and varying the pressure by changing the stroke. A ring or a cylinder may be developed in a 90-deg. die by giving the plate a series of light impressions.

As previously stated, it is cheaper to bend than to weld a joint. Consider, for example, the U-shape in Fig. 10–4. The man-hour rate of producing this form from one piece of plate by bending is estimated along with the rate of fabricating it from three plates using welding, as in Fig. 10–5.

FORMING IN A PRESS BRAKE

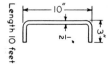

Fig. 10-4. Profile of one-piece channel formed in a press brake.

Operation	Man-Hours
Lay out	0.35
Shear	1.00
Bend	3.00
Straighten	0.50
Total	4.85

FABRICATION BY WELDING

Operation	Man-Hours
Lay out	0.35
Shear	1.50
Burn	1.50
Weld	3.50
Fit up and tack	1.50
Grind ⎱ Clean ⎰	1.25
Straighten	0.75
Total	10.35

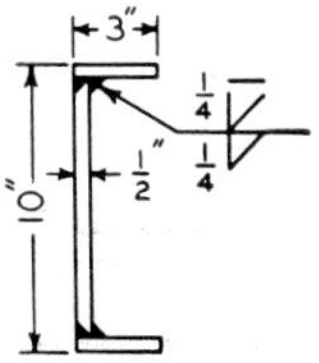

Fig. 10-5. Profile of a three-piece welded channel.

The estimate shows that the man-hour rate for forming the channel section from a single piece of plate is approximately one-half the man-hour rate required for welding the same size of channel from three plates. This ratio will vary, of course, according to the thickness and the length of the channel section. In all cases, however, bending will be found the more economical method. If a standard rolled channel can be used in place of press-brake channel shown above, then the rolled shape is the most economical section, since it costs little more than the plate alone. There may be instances where the well-rounded corners of the press-brake channel section will influence the choice.

Although the press brake is used in a wide variety of forming operations, it must be understood that the work is not held to such exact dimensions as the hundredths and thousandths of an inch possible in a die stamping. For press-brake work, the tolerance will usually vary between $\frac{1}{32}$ and $\frac{1}{8}$ in., depending upon the size and shape of the plate. There is some springback of the metal on removal of the ram just as there is a springback in a stamping when the pressure is removed. The greatest variation in press-brake bending results from the operators' inability to line up the plate so that the ram will strike along an inscribed line. There will also be variations in the angle of bend, which the operators must check with a template. The designer must expect rather liberal tolerances in the work, especially if curved sections and complicated shapes are developed. As in all manual work, the quality is largely dependent upon the skill of the operators; and it is amazing what an experienced crew can develop in the way of matched parts. The weldment fitters are accustomed to variations in the steel they handle. Mill plates and rolled sections are all subject to variations in both thickness and straightness, but they can usually be skillfully worked.

The press brake can be used to bend metal hot as well as cold, so that S.A.E. 1045 steel plates are preheated before bending to prevent cracking. Heavy S.A.E. 1020 plates are also preheated to avoid bending cracks. Rolled steel bends most easily if the impression is perpendicular to the direction of rolling. Difficulty is sometimes experienced even with light plates when it is necessary to make the ram impression parallel to the direction of rolling. Cracks may form in plates that have been finished at too low a temperature. Cold-rolled plates are also liable to crack on bending cold. Ordinary hot-rolled steel plates up to $\frac{3}{4}$ in. thick are usually bent in any direction without difficulty. The low-alloy high-strength steels also bend easily.

COURTESY CLEVELAND CRANE AND ENGINEERING CO.

Fig. 10-6. Forming a wide U in the press brake.

The designer is not interested in the details of brake operation, but he should know certain of its limitations and make his designs in accordance with them. Tanks are usually made up of a U-section and two end plates (Fig. 10–6). For the plate to clear the ram on the second bend, dimension *B* of Fig. 10–7 should be at least equal to *A* and preferably greater. Figure 10–7 also shows the open throat dimension on a press brake. This dimension represents the widest flange that can be bent in lengths equal to or greater than the full die length of the machine. If the bent flange is less than the throat dimension, it is possible to bend a continuous length of 20 or 30 ft. by shifting the work in the press. For bending plates that come within the outer frame of the press, it is possible to bend a flange of much greater width than this throat dimension.

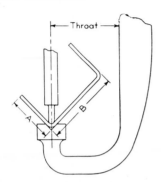

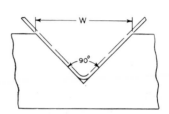

Fig. 10-7. Open-throat dimensions on a press brake.

Fig. 10-8. Ninety-degree die for bending.

Figure 10–8 shows a 90-deg. die for bending. The average pressure per foot of length in tons is given by the following equation:

$$\text{Pressure} = \frac{\text{plate thickness} \times \text{ult. strength of plate}}{125 \times \text{die ratio (die width to plate thickness)}}$$

Figure 10–9 shows some of the types of dies used in making odd shapes. The procedure followed is self-explanatory.

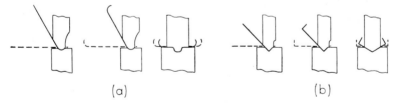

(a)   (b)

Fig. 10-9. Press-brake work.

Figure 10–10 (pages 150–159) shows sketches of 250 different parts that have been produced with the press brake. These sketches will give the designer a better understanding of what can be accomplished in the forming of metals. No dimensions are shown, though

1 ANGLE	2 OPEN BEND	3 CHANNEL	4 CHANNEL	5 TRUCK BODY
6 TROUGH	7 CHANNEL	8 GUTTER	9 SQUARE TUBE	10 OBLONG TUBE
11 REVERSE BEND	12 PLAIN RISER	13 FASCIA	14 TREAD	15 CONTINUOUS STAIR
16 TREAD & RISER	17 TREAD & RISER	18 TREAD & RISER	19 TREAD & RISER	20 TREAD & RISER
21 HALF ROUND GUTTER	22 CENTER STRIP	23 COVE	24 THRESHOLD	25 CHUTE

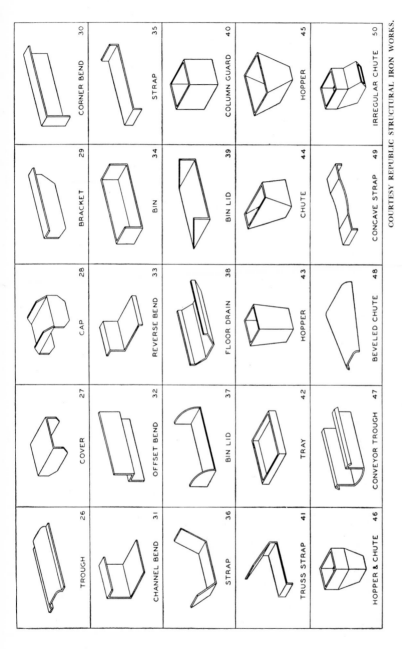

Fig. 10-10. Samples of plate and bar bending.

TROUGH 26

COVER 27

CAP 28

BRACKET 29

CORNER BEND 30

CHANNEL BEND 31

OFFSET BEND 32

REVERSE BEND 33

BIN 34

STRAP 35

STRAP 36

BIN LID 37

FLOOR DRAIN 38

BIN LID 39

COLUMN GUARD 40

TRUSS STRAP 41

TRAY 42

HOPPER 43

CHUTE 44

HOPPER 45

HOPPER & CHUTE 46

CONVEYOR TROUGH 47

BEVELED CHUTE 48

CONCAVE STRAP 49

IRREGULAR CHUTE 50

51 U STRAP	52 BOX STRAP	53 BENT BAR	54 BAR CLIP	55 BAR CLIP
56 BRACKET	57 GUTTER	58 BRACKET	59 BRACKET	60 CONVEYOR PLATE
61 Z BAR	62 SPECIAL ANGLE	63 THRESHOLD	64 V BEND	65 V BEND
66 HOOK	67 ANGLE BEND	68 OFFSET BEND	69 OFFSET BEND	70 SPECIAL BEND
71 DOUBLE BAR FORK	72 ANGLE BEND	73 BOX CHANNEL	74 DOOR FRAME	75 BAR SUPPORT

152

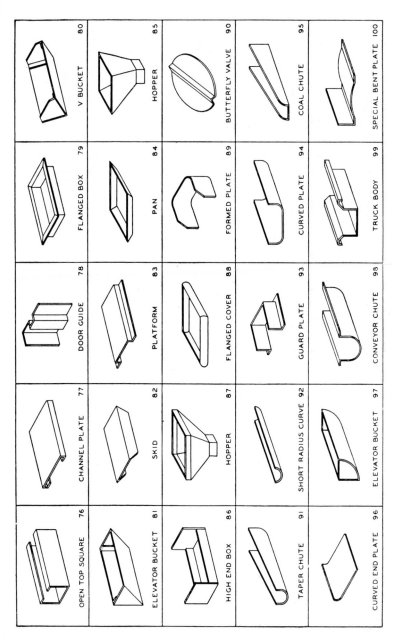

OPEN TOP SQUARE 76	CHANNEL PLATE 77	DOOR GUIDE 78	FLANGED BOX 79	V BUCKET 80
ELEVATOR BUCKET 81	SKID 82	PLATFORM 83	PAN 84	HOPPER 85
HIGH END BOX 86	HOPPER 87	FLANGED COVER 88	FORMED PLATE 89	BUTTERFLY VALVE 90
TAPER CHUTE 91	SHORT RADIUS CURVE 92	GUARD PLATE 93	CURVED PLATE 94	COAL CHUTE 95
CURVED END PLATE 96	ELEVATOR BUCKET 97	CONVEYOR CHUTE 98	TRUCK BODY 99	SPECIAL BENT PLATE 100

Fig. 10-10. (Cont.) Samples of plate and bar bending.

153

TROUGH 101	FLANGE BRACKET 102	HANGER PLATE 103	TROUGH 104	CONVEYOR TROUGH 105
GUTTER 106	AUTO BODY 107	BRACKET 108	STRUT 109	SHELL 110
ROOF CAP 111	V STRAP 112	BEVEL TOP PLATE 113	V STRAP 114	THRESHOLD 115
FORM 116	TRUCK BODY SIDE 117	DOOR BUCK 118	CURVED PLATE 119	SPECIAL HOPPER 120
BEVEL SILL 121	GUIDE 122	DOUBLE V BEND 123	COVER PLATE 124	BENT IN FLANGE 125

154

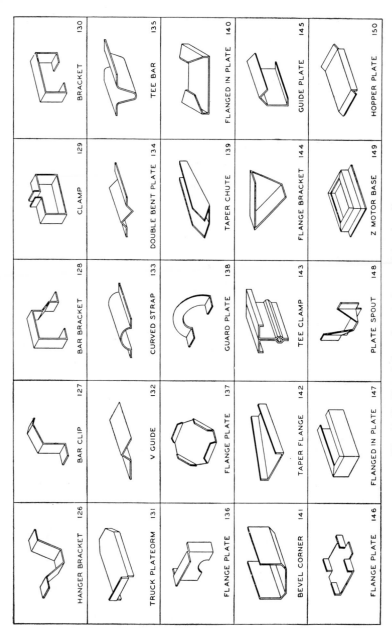

HANGER BRACKET 126	BAR CLIP 127	BAR BRACKET 128	CLAMP 129	BRACKET 130
TRUCK PLATFORM 131	V GUIDE 132	CURVED STRAP 133	DOUBLE BENT PLATE 134	TEE BAR 135
FLANGE PLATE 136	FLANGE PLATE 137	GUARD PLATE 138	TAPER CHUTE 139	FLANGED IN PLATE 140
BEVEL CORNER 141	TAPER FLANGE 142	TEE CLAMP 143	FLANGE BRACKET 144	GUIDE PLATE 145
FLANGE PLATE 146	FLANGED IN PLATE 147	PLATE SPOUT 148	Z MOTOR BASE 149	HOPPER PLATE 150

Fig. 10-10. (Cont.) Samples of plate and bar bending.

155

TRUCK BOX 151	BOX BRACKET 152	CONVEYOR CHUTE 153	BUCKET 154	V BOTTOM BOX 155
ZEE BEND 156	CONVEYOR CHUTE 157	FLANGED CHUTE 158	FLANGED PLATE 159	GUIDE PLATE 160
TROUGH 161	CURVED CHUTE 162	CHUTE 163	GUIDE PLATE 164	CHUTE 165
GUIDE PLATE 166	CONVEYOR PLATE 167	CAP PLATE 168	CONVEYOR PLATE 169	BENT PLATE 170
DOUBLE BEND 171	MOULDING 172	BRACKET 173	BRACKET 174	SPECIAL BRACKET 175

156

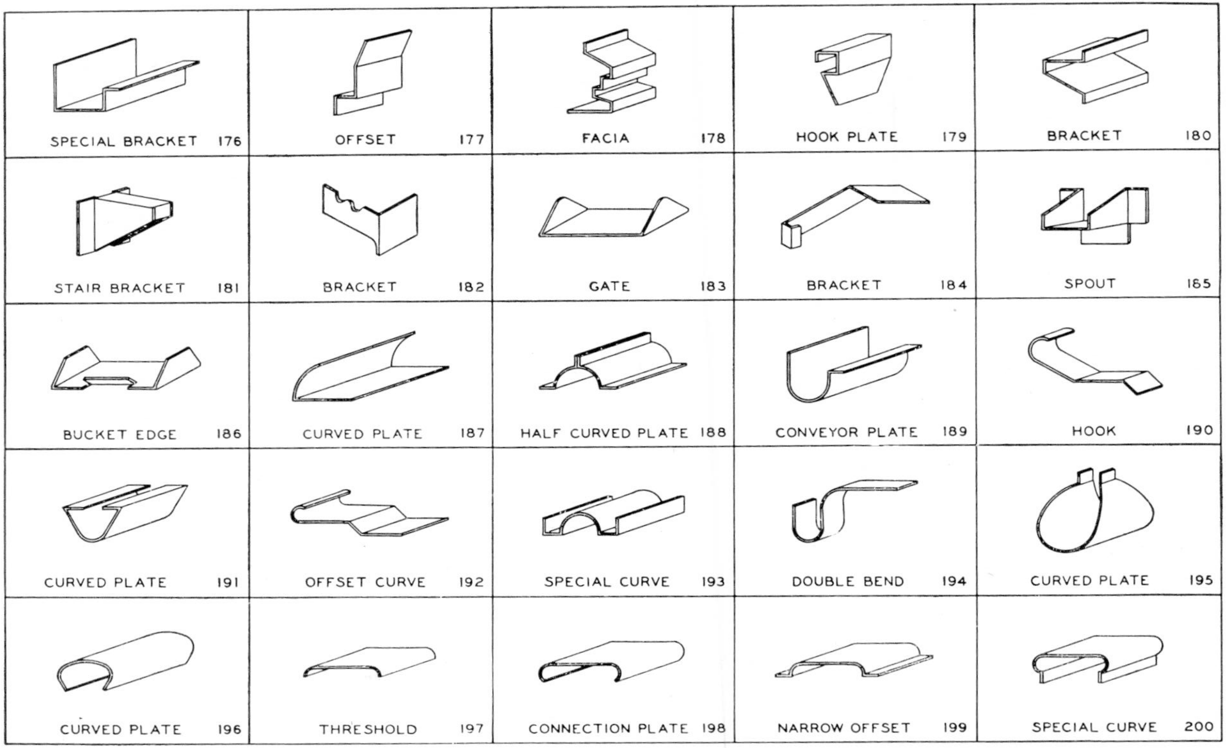

SPECIAL BRACKET 176	OFFSET 177	FACIA 178	HOOK PLATE 179	BRACKET 180
STAIR BRACKET 181	BRACKET 182	GATE 183	BRACKET 184	SPOUT 165
BUCKET EDGE 186	CURVED PLATE 187	HALF CURVED PLATE 188	CONVEYOR PLATE 189	HOOK 190
CURVED PLATE 191	OFFSET CURVE 192	SPECIAL CURVE 193	DOUBLE BEND 194	CURVED PLATE 195
CURVED PLATE 196	THRESHOLD 197	CONNECTION PLATE 198	NARROW OFFSET 199	SPECIAL CURVE 200

Fig. 10-10. (Cont.) Samples of plate and bar bending.

MOLD 205	MOLD 210	NOSING 215	MOLD 220	SPECIAL PLATE 225
MOLD 204	MOLD 209	MOLD 214	HINGE 219	PAN 224
TROUGH 203	MOLD 208	SPECIAL CURVE 213	CONNECTION PLATE 218	DOUBLE CURVE 223
GUIDE PLATE 202	MOLD 207	NOSING 212	TREAD 217	SPECIAL TROUGH 222
MOLD 201	MOLD 206	MOLD 211	NOSING 216	MOLD 221

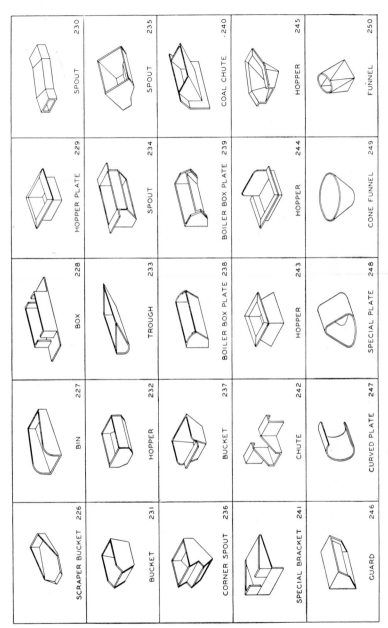

Fig. 10-10. (Cont.) Samples of plate and bar bending.

SCRAPER BUCKET 226	BIN 227	BOX 228	HOPPER PLATE 229	SPOUT 230
BUCKET 231	HOPPER 232	TROUGH 233	SPOUT 234	SPOUT 235
CORNER SPOUT 236	BUCKET 237	BOILER BOX PLATE 238	BOILER BOX PLATE 239	COAL CHUTE .240
SPECIAL BRACKET 241	CHUTE 242	HOPPER 243	HOPPER 244	HOPPER 245
GUARD 246	CURVED PLATE 247	SPECIAL PLATE 248	CONE FUNNEL 249	FUNNEL 250

159

in most cases the parts are made from rather heavy plate, ⅛ to
⅝ in. in thickness and from 1 ft. to 10 ft. in over-all size. No. 131
may be readily identified as an industrial truck platform. Many of
these shapes have replaced castings and forgings, since if the
weldery has suitable dies available, it is usually cheaper to form
in a press brake than to cast or forge when the sections can be
formed from a single plate.

Rolling

Power rolls are used by the weldery in forming cylinders, cones,
rings, and other shapes from cold plate. In order to develop a
true circle, it is necessary to pre-bend the ends for several inches,
usually in a press brake. An alternative method is to trim the ends
after rolling and remove the flat portion.

Since it is sometimes difficult to obtain heavy-walled seamless
pipe of rather large diameter, the weldery frequently makes its own

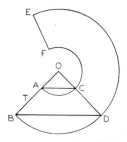

pipe sections by rolling or bulldozing and
then vee-welding the joints. The method of
forming a conical shaped section is illustrated in Fig. 10–11.

ABCD of thickness *T* represents the coni-
cal-shaped section. The sides of the cone are
extended to *O,* and circles are inscribed with
O as a center and *OA* and *OB* as radii. The
circumference of a circle having a diameter
of *BD* is then measured off on the circum-

Fig. 10-11. Cone design.

ference *BDE,* and the circumference of the
circle having a diameter of *AC* is measured off along *ACF.* Plate
ABEF is the shape required to roll a cone *ABCD.* Large cones are
sometimes laid out in two or more sections. Cylinders and cones may
also be developed by the brake method (Figs. 10–12 and 10–13).

Special rolling machines are available for rolling angles, channels, I-beams, and bars. In forming rings, there is always the
question whether it is cheaper to burn the ring out of a plate or
to edge-roll it from bar stock and weld it. The thickness of the
plate usually determines the method. Rings made from thin plate
are always burned unless the diameters are large and close together. For heavy plate, it is usually necessary to estimate both

ways, since there is always considerable loss in the center slug. The thickness and the radius of bend are important.

Three applications of the bulldozer being used in special forming operations are shown in Figs. 10–14, 10–15, and 10–16. Figure

Fig. 10-12. Press brake used in forming a cylinder.

10–14 shows a rim for a large gear being formed from S.A.E. 1045 steel. Figure 10–15 shows a special set of dies used for bending channel sections previously formed in the press brake. Figure 10–16 shows a rib being formed into a U-section.

Tangent-bending and Contour-forming Machines

Machines of this type are used in developing a curved contour in special bent sections. Although the processes have been used on metal of $\frac{1}{4}$ in. thickness and greater, the majority of applications

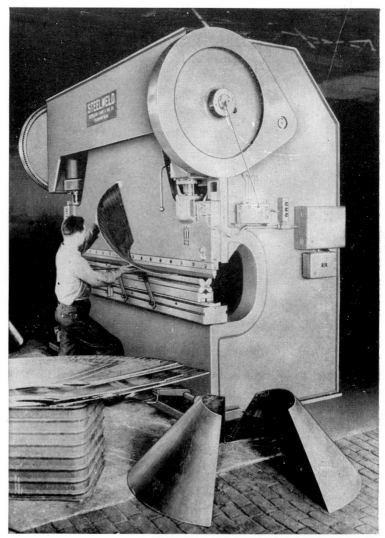

COURTESY CLEVELAND CRANE AND ENGINEERING CO.

Fig. 10-13. Press brake used to form cone.

have been in light sheet metal. Numerous metals and alloys are formed such as steel, stainless steel, aluminum, magnesium, brass, and bronze. Two methods have been used extensively: tangent

COURTESY CLEVELAND CRANE AND ENGINEERING CO.

Fig. 10-14. Forming the S.A.E. 1045 steel rim for a large-diameter gear blank in a bulldozer.

COURTESY CLEVELAND CRANE AND ENGINEERING CO.

Fig. 10-15. Forming a special vee shape out of channel sections previously formed in the press brake.

COURTESY CLEVELAND CRANE AND ENGINEERING CO.

Fig. 10-16. Forming a special rib section in the bulldozer.

COURTESY CYRIL BATH CO.

Fig. 10-17. Tangent-bending machine used in forming refrigerator shells. (First operation.)

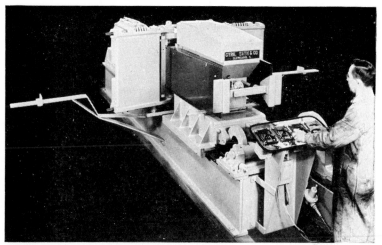

COURTESY CYRIL BATH CO.

Fig. 10-18. Tangent-bending machine used in forming refrigerator shells. (Second operation.)

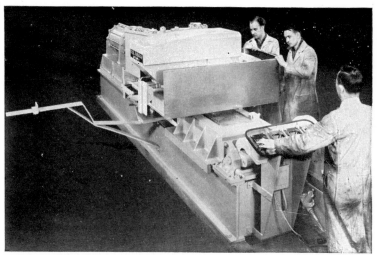

COURTESY CYRIL BATH CO.

Fig. 10-19. Tangent-bending machine used in forming refrigerator shells.' (Third operation.)

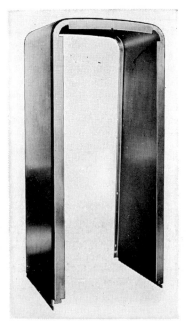

COURTESY CYRIL BATH CO.

Fig. 10-20. The finished refrigerator shell.

COURTESY CYRIL BATH CO.

Fig. 10-21. The contour-bending machine starting to form the rail section for a bus.

bending and stretch bending. In tangent bending, material is built up at the zone of curvature, and the section is strengthened; in stretch bending, metal is removed in the bending operation just as in the braking method. These processes have been used extensively for creating streamlined contours in cabinet designs such as radios, metal furniture, and washing machines. Other applications

COURTESY CYRIL BATH CO.

Fig. 10-22. The finished rail section. Note the final position of the rotating table, which carries the forming die.

are numerous in the field of aircraft and automobiles, store fixtures, and light machinery frames.

The tangent bender has been used quite generally for forming refrigerator shells. Figures 10–17, 10–18, and 10–19 show the stages used in forming the shell from a one-piece channel section previously flanged in a press brake. The device illustrated here is a tangent-bending machine. Figure 10–20 shows the refrigerator shell as it is produced by this process. The tangent bender forms the flanged sections into the final U-shape without distortion of the flanged edge, eliminating notching, welding, and grinding at the double-radius corners at a considerable saving in cost.

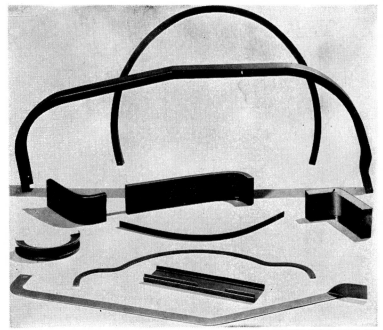

Fig. 10-23. Some of the many shapes developed by the contour-bending process.

Figures 10–21 and 10–22 show a contour-forming machine developing a rib for a bus body. Figure 10–23 shows a great variety of shapes made by this process.

Small machine tools have welded bases made up of rather light metal. It is possible to develop streamlined designs in weldments of this type by tangent-bending and contour-forming principles, just as they are applied to refrigerators, radios, aircraft, and other items, provided the quantities are sufficient. It is also possible that the designer will work in various metals and color schemes to make the machine more attractive. There is no reason why a machine base should not have the same beauty of line and color as an automobile or a radio cabinet.

In the future, designers may follow the same principles as those governing automobile-body design and build a rigid frame of rolled sections capable of supporting the machine load and covering this frame with a light metal shell in streamlined style. At present, the designer frequently attempts to combine both style and strength in heavy weldments, but strength demands heavy plates that are difficult to form. The heavier the plate, the more limited are the forming operations that can be applied to it. On the other hand, light metal forms easily, permitting a wider scope of forming operations. Double-radius bends and graceful curves and twists are no problem in light-metal forming but are very difficult and costly in heavy-plate work. The cost of handling, fitting up, welding, shearing, and bending—indeed, the cost of any operation on metal —increases sharply with an increase in the thickness and weight of the material.

Flanging and Dishing

Flanged sections, with and without dishing, are formed cold in the lighter sections by many boiler shops. Only a few of the largest fabricating subdivisions of steel companies are equipped to flange and dish the heavier plate sections. These are all hot-forming operations.

Die Forgings

Although drop forgings are not generally used in the fabrication of a machine base, they are used extensively for such machine parts as gears, cams, levers, axles, shafts, and hubs. Forgings are selected because of their uniform high quality and dependability for machine parts requiring a combination of odd shape and contour plus unusually high strength and toughness.

The die cost in the manufacture of a forging is of course high, and large quantities of duplicate parts are necessary to justify this cost. Forgings are not limited to steel and its alloys but include many metals and alloys such as copper, brass, bronze, aluminum alloys, stainless steels, and magnesium alloys (see Table 10–1).

The mechanical press is generally used in forming small non-ferrous die forgings that weigh under 30 lb. The board drop hammer is used in shaping small elements up to 15 lb., provided they are simple in design. The material may be low-carbon steel, copper, aluminum, or magnesium alloy. The steam drop hammer is the most economical device for forgings weighing between 15 and 300 lb. Above 300 lb., the hydraulic press is commonly used.

TABLE 10–1

<small>CHARACTERISTICS OF COMMON FORGING METALS *</small>

Metal	Die life	Production	Machinability	Uses
S.A.E. 1020	100	100	100	Small parts
S.A.E. 1030	98	98	104	Small parts
S.A.E. 1035	95	96	87	Medium parts
S.A.E. 1040	95	96	81	Medium parts
S.A.E. 1045	90	93	78	Large parts
S.A.E. 2340	84	89	82	Gears, axles
S.A.E. 3140	85	90	74	Gears, axles
S.A.E. 3250	77	84	69	High-strength parts
S.A.E. 4140	84	90	83	Aircraft parts
S.A.E. 5140	84	89	76	Gears, axles
S.A.E. 6150	78	84	67	Antifatigue forgings
S.A.E. 30915	20–65	80	50	Corrosion, heat
S.A.E. 51410	30–70	85	80	Corrosion, heat
Forging Cu	110	125	125	Press forgings
Forging Br	115	107	200	Press forgings
Naval Br	110	103	160	Press forgings
Monel	20–65	30–60	59	Corrosion, heat

* Ratios are shown as compared to standard S.A.E. 1020 forging steel. From *Forging Handbook 1943*, American Society for Metals, Cleveland.

Table 10–2 shows commercial forging tolerances for different weights. Forging dies are usually machined to the lower limits specified for a part. When the impression has worn to the upper limits, the die is scrapped or resunk. It is customary to allow $\frac{1}{16}$ to $\frac{1}{2}$ in., depending upon the size of the forging on surfaces to be machined.

The most common use of forgings for weldments is the corner piece where there are double-radius bends. Some of these sections are shown in Fig. 4–6. Forgings are also used for plate thicknesses exceeding stock maximums or for rounds when the diameter exceeds about 7 in.

Steel Castings

Steel castings are sometimes used in weldments when small quantity lots of odd shapes and difficult contours are desired, since the pattern cost is generally much less than the cost of a forging die. Electric-furnace steel is preferred because it gives a cleaner

TABLE 10–2

FORGING THICKNESS TOLERANCES

Net weight maximum, pounds	Commercial		Close	
	Plus, inches	Minus, inches	Plus, inches	Minus, inches
0.2	0.008	0.024	0.004	0.012
0.4	0.009	0.027	0.005	0.015
0.6	0.010	0.030	0.005	0.015
0.8	0.011	0.033	0.006	0.018
1.0	0.012	0.036	0.006	0.018
2.0	0.015	0.045	0.008	0.024
3.0	0.017	0.051	0.009	0.027
4.0	0.018	0.054	0.009	0.027
5.0	0.019	0.057	0.010	0.030
10.0	0.022	0.066	0.011	0.033
20.0	0.026	0.078	0.013	0.039
30.0	0.030	0.090	0.015	0.045
40.0	0.034	0.102	0.017	0.051
50.0	0.038	0.114	0.019	0.057
60.0	0.042	0.126	0.021	0.063
70.0	0.046	0.138	0.023	0.069
80.0	0.050	0.150	0.025	0.075
90.0	0.054	0.162	0.027	0.081
100.0	0.058	0.174	0.029	0.087

TABLE, COURTESY OF MACHINE DESIGN

steel that causes less trouble in welding. The composition and physical properties of steel castings used in weldments should be specified. The plain carbon steels are best for weldability, and it is preferable that the carbon content be well under 0.35 per cent.

Die Stamping

Stamping operations may be divided into three groups: shearing, drawing, and squeezing. The shearing operations include perforating, punching, shearing, slitting, parting, notching, trimming, and blanking. In drawing, the metal is formed by one or a series of die impressions, with annealing sometimes required between steps. The shape of the stamping may vary from a simple bracket to a large complicated piece with curves and irregular contours. Squeezing operations include swaging, coining, and embossing. In all stamping operations, the work on the metal is done entirely beyond the yield point.

Die stamping is used extensively in machinery design and for such items as oil pans, gear housings, tool boxes, louver doors, and switch panels. There is scarcely a machine tool without at least one stamping in evidence.

Die-stamping operations require high-volume production to absorb the high die cost, particularly for complicated shapes. The parts must run into thousands before the designer can even consider the process, although for certain designs involving very simple layout it is practical to build a die to make less than a thousand units. The enormous pressures required to form large complicated shapes exclude heavy plate from consideration. It is in the field of light sheet metal that the stamping reigns supreme. Automatic stamping machines are now in use that will blank out a thousand pieces per minute, the material being fed into the unit from coils.

Stampings are made from almost any metal having good cold-working properties, but those which work-harden appreciably require more power than those which do not. Cold stampings are made on plate up to $3/4$ in., and hot stampings are made on plate up to $3\frac{1}{2}$ in. The size may vary over broad limits. Cold-rolled sheet steel (0.05 to 0.20 per cent carbon) may be easily stamped, as well as copper, brass, bronze, stainless steel, and aluminum. As the carbon content of steel increases, the shearing and punching power requirements increase also, a maximum carbon content of 0.35 per cent usually being set for cold-forming.

Deep-drawing steel with carbon below 0.10 per cent is the preferred material for stamping. Cold-rolled strip sheet steel has a good surface and the best drawing properties. Manufacturers have set a top limit of 33 per cent elongation in drawing operations. Steel with a high sulphur content does not draw well. Stainless steel is excellent material for cold-working when it is thoroughly annealed, but it work-hardens rapidly and requires much more press and shearing power than a low-carbon steel.

Die stamping differs from press-brake work in that the dies are accurately made and the material is formed to exact contours within close tolerances. Also, as in flame cutting, the stamping scrap metal loss is considerable and must be held to a minimum.

Tolerances

Special sizing operations such as coining and shaving render extremely close tolerances. Shaved spur gears are held to a total tolerance of 0.001 in. The greatest difficulties in holding close tolerances result from mill variations in the thickness and size of the sheet metal. Surface grinding is sometimes necessary to attain the required flatness, especially on large flat surfaces. Hard materials are the most difficult to hold because of spring-back tendencies when the pressure is removed. Production tolerances of ± 0.005 in. can be held under certain satisfactory conditions, and even 0.001 in. can be held for circular shapes, outside dimensions, and hole locations, though ± 0.01 in. is generally permissible.

Fig. 10-24. Nesting.

Nesting, a method of utilizing stock economically, is represented in Fig. 10–24.

Any light machine-frame design that is made up in quantities of 100 or more per month should be analyzed for the possibility of fabrication from stampings. For example, the production of a certain lathe reached a point at which it was cheaper to stamp the oil pan, whereas it had previously been formed in a press brake.

Summary of Welded Components

Up to this point, the various components used in weldment design have been discussed. To summarize, these are the plate or rolled section sheared or saw-cut to size or length, the plate burned to template, the section formed in a press brake, the section developed by rolling, the flanged and dished sections, the special form created by tangent bending and contour forming, the forging, the steel casting, and the die stamping. Although various alloys and metals were included in the discussions, the designer should understand that in relation to weldment design, low-carbon hot-rolled steel is the metal used in the largest proportion of such weldments, and that any forgings, castings, or stampings used are also of the low-carbon grade and quite weldable. The above components may each be made an integral part of the weldment by being welded to it.

In any discussion of machinery components based strictly on shape or design, two additional components should be included, though neither type is ever welded to the body of the weldment. These are the die casting and the plastic shape used as machine elements and attached to the unit by machine screws or bolts.

Die Castings

Sand molds are single-purpose molds and are destroyed after the metal has solidified in them. Permanent molds, made of metal capable of withstanding high temperatures, greatly reduce the time of the casting process, although they are applicable only to small castings and are economical only for large quantity lots.

Several methods have been developed for making castings by use of permanent molds, as follows: gravity casting, slush casting, pressed casting, centrifugal casting, and die casting. The die-casting process came rapidly to the fore during World War II and is now challenging the sand casting and the forging. Although die castings are seldom used as integral parts of welded machine bases, there is considerable use for them in certain small machine parts and accessories.

Die casting is a method of forcing molten metal under pressure into a metal die. The pressure in the die may vary between 5 and 15,000 lb. per square inch, though small parts cast in metals of low melting temperatures may require only from 80 to 125 lb. per square inch until solidification is complete.

The advantages of die casting over sand casting are listed as follows:

(1) The rapidity of the process, since both mold and core are permanent

(2) A smoother surface obtained from the metal mold

(3) Little work required to prepare the casting for plating or other finishing operations

(4) More accurate control of the size of the casting

(5) No machining required

(6) No allowance necessary for variation in thickness

(7) Strong, dense metal free of sand inclusions

(8) Possibility of casting threads and holes and eliminating their machining operation

The high cost of the machine and the dies is a drawback, as is the rapid decrease in the life of the mold due to high temperatures. Moreover, there are limitations as to shape and size of the die casting, and the work is generally limited to certain metals of low melting temperature, such as lead, tin, aluminum, magnesium, and zinc. Magnesium die castings were extensively used during World War II for engine and instrument parts for aircraft. Die-cast alloys not so widely used are brass, bronze, cast iron, and steel. Their high melting points force up the temperatures for the process and cut down the mold life, whereas the low-temperature metals and alloys have melting points below 1000° F. and permit low production and die-maintenance costs. As casting temperatures increase, special steels are required to reduce the oxidation and checking of the die surface.

Some of the factors that influence the selection of die-cast alloys are the physical properties, weight, machinability, resistance to corrosion, surface, and cost.

(1) *Zinc-Base Alloys.* Alloys of zinc are the most common by far, since they have excellent casting properties, considerable strength, a smooth finish, and a low melting point for minimum casting cost. One of the most widely used zinc alloys has the following composition:

A.S.T.M. XXI—S.A.E. 921

Metal	Per Cent
Aluminum	4.10
Copper	2.70
Magnesium	0.03
Zinc	Remainder

Melting point: 733.6°F
Shrinkage: 0.149 in. per foot
Ultimate tensile strength: 47,300 p.s.i.

Another important zinc alloy is the following:

A.S.T.M. XXIII—S.A.E. 903

Metal	Per Cent
Aluminum	4.1
Magnesium	0.04
Zinc	Remainder

(2) *Lead-Base Alloys.* These alloys generally contain about 17 per cent antimony, which causes hardness and reduces shrinkage.

They are easily cast and have good physical properties, with a low melting point of 570° F. They are used principally for light-duty bearings, battery parts, and X-ray shields.

(3) *Tin-Base Alloys.* These alloys, known as "Babbitt metal," are chiefly used for bearings in internal-combustion engines.

(4) *Magnesium-Base Alloys.* These are the lightest of all the die-cast alloys, being two-thirds the weight of those of aluminum. They are more machinable than aluminum alloys, but the price per pound is higher. The best-known die-cast magnesium alloy is Dow-metal K, of the following specification:

A.S.T.M. B94–39T ALLOY 12

Metal	Per Cent
Aluminum	10.0
Zinc	0.3
Manganese	0.2
Silicon	0.7
Magnesium	Remainder

Alloys of magnesium require a casting temperature of about 1250° F. They are strong and light, being used for portable tools and household appliances.

(5) *Copper-Base Alloys.* The chief advantage of brass and bronze is their high strength when resistance to corrosion is necessary. Their melting points are high, ranging from 1600 to 1900° F. They are used mainly for hardware, electrical machine parts, small gears, marine fittings, chemical apparatus, and automotive fittings.

YELLOW BRASS

Metal	Per Cent
Copper	60.0
Tin	1.0
Lead	0.75
Manganese	0.25
Zinc	Remainder
Ultimate tensile strength:	65,000 p.s.i.

Plastic Molding

No discussion dealing with the various processes of forming metals would be complete without some reference to plastic molding materials. Some companies are specializing in plastic molded designs for the machine-tool field. Plastics have been used for feed dials, gear housings, and switch boxes; and there is undoubtedly a place for the transparent grades in machine design when it is desired to observe the moving parts in motion. Cellulose derivatives, resins, and protein matter are the principal plastic materials. They have poor strength and little resistance to heat, corrosion, and oxidation. Their advantages are lightness, high electrical resistance, excellent surface finish and colors, and a good degree of transparency.

Estimating Welded Machine-Base Costs

T HE DESIGNER should be cost-conscious. He is first of all concerned with the problem of laying out the design that is the most economical to fabricate, and secondarily with the cost of the weldment as compared to the cost of casting a base that will accomplish the same purpose. It is the purpose here to show an actual weldment design and to describe the procedure of estimating fabrication cost. Because of fluctuations in prices, it is impractical to show exact costs. The purpose is rather to illustrate a method of approach, and no further significance should be attached to cost items.

All welderies maintain a staff of estimators who can readily appraise the cost of construction in their particular plant. It is advantageous, though, for the designer to be able to estimate his own work, at least in a general way, since such preliminary studies frequently point to further simplification in the design. Weldments of a similar pattern that vary only in size and minor detail will have a cost per pound proportional to the weight; thus, after an estimate has been made for a particular size, it is simple to determine the weight of steel required and the corresponding cost for another size.

Figure 11–1 illustrates the construction of a base that has been produced in a commercial weldery. The designer shows a plan view, a side, and an end elevation. Since this particular design involved considerable inside detail, section drawings were added to indicate the construction more clearly. The most frequent mistake made by designers is the failure to show sufficient detail sections in their drawings. This drawing is made to a 1:8 scale,

178

which is quite satisfactory for the particular size of base. A 1:8 scale often fails to bring out the detail clearly, though it is frequently used on large bases of simple construction. The designer has specified that all fillet welds are to be ¼ in. and continuous, except where noted. For the exceptions, he has used standard American Welding Society symbols to indicate the type of weld desired. In designs that permit a general specification of the welding, it is of course preferable to specify by note rather than to use detail welding symbols.

The designer has used ⅜ in. plate for the side walls, top, bottom, and various ribs. Practically all compartments must be oiltight, so double continuous welds are specified. The corners are rounded with a generous radius. In the notes, the designer has specified stress relief and the type of finish desired. Information of this kind should always be noted on the drawing and placed in a conspicuous place. It must be remembered that the drawing goes to the template men, the fitters, the welders, the engineers—in fact to all who take part in the construction of the base. *The weldery always builds the weldment in accordance with the drawing.*

In this design, the various inside ribs are shown by section, although in some designs, the draftsman shows a separate layout of the ribs and marks them "rib *A*," "rib *B*," and so on. A similar tag is then attached to each rib on the plan drawing to make the identification complete. Such detailed drawings of ribs are very clear and are much more practical than complete sections. The work of the template maker and the estimator is simplified by such a procedure.

The first step in estimating is to prepare a complete bill of material. The bill of material for this job (Fig. 11–2) was prepared by the Rex Welding Co. for the Moon Machine Co., and the inquiry specified 50 weldments as shown on their blueprint No. 200-G. Each item on the bill is numbered on the drawing so that the estimator can itemize the welding and cutting operations. The number also permits rapid checking and identification of parts. Item 1 specifies 2PL (plates) 27⅛ × ⅜ in., weighing 34.58 pounds per foot. These plates are 4 ft. 1½ in. long and hence total 8.25 ft. in length. Multiplying 34.58 by 8.25 gives 286 lb. The "b" at the right on the bill of material signifies that this particular size of plate carries a base price; that is, there is no extra added cost for size.

THE REX WELDING CO.
220 King Ave.
Philadelphia, Pa.

Subject: **Estimate**	Date:	**Dec. 10, 1949**
For: **The Moon Machine Co.**		
410 South St.	Drawing No.:	**200-G**
Philadelphia, Pa.	Fig. by:	**E.A.W.**
Buyer: **Dwight Jenkins, P.A.**	Chk'd by:	**T.S.G.**

Required: **50 Weldments, Drawing No. 200-G.**

Item	No. Pieces	Section	Weight Pounds	Length	Total Linear Feet	Total Weight	Extras $ per cwt.
1	2PL	27-1/8" x 3/8"	34.58	4' 1-1/2"	8.25	286	b
2	1PL	19-3/4" x 3/8"	25.25	2' 4-1/4"	2.36	60	b
3	4PL	4" x 2-1/4"	31.21	4"	1.34	42	.30
4	4PL	3" x 3/8"	3.83	4"	1.34	6	b
5	2PL	2-5/8" x 1-1/2"	13.47	4-1/2"	0.75	11	b
6	2PL	2-5/8" x 3/8"	3.37	3"	0.50	2	b
7	1PL	4" x 3/8"	5.10	1' 7-3/4"	1.67	9	b
8	1PL	19-3/4" x 3/8"	25.25	2' 4-1/4"	2.36	60	b
9	1PL	7-1/4" x 3/8"	9.24	1' 7-3/4"	1.67	16	b
10	1PL	19-3/4" x 3/8"	25.25	2' 9-1/4"	1.83	47	b
11	1PL	19-3/4" x 3/8"	25.25	2' 1/2"	2.05	52	b
12	2PL	1" x 3/8"	1.28	5-1/4"	0.90	2	b
13	1PL	8-1/4" x 3/8"	10.52	1' 7-3/4"	1.67	18	b
14	3PL	4-1/2" x 3/8"	5.74	1' 2-3/8"	3.63	21	b
15	1RD	3" diam.	24.03	1-1/2"	0.13	4	.20
16	1PL	2" x 2-1/4"	15.51	2-1/2"	0.21	4	.30
17	1RD	2-1/2" diam.	16.69	6-1/4"	0.52	9	.15
18	1RD	2-3/4" diam.	20.19	3/4"	0.10	3	.20
19	1PL	6-1/4" x 3/8"	7.97	6-3/4"	0.57	5	b
20	1PL	4-1/4" x 3/8"	5.42	6-1/4"	0.57	3	b
21	1RD	2" diam.	10.68	1-1/2"	0.13	2	.10
22	1PL	5-1/2" x 3/4"	14.03	1' 3-1/2"	1.30	19	b
23	1PL	3-5/8" x 1/2"	6.33	6"	0.50	4	b
24	1B	5" x 3/4"	12.75	2' 3-1/4"	2.30	30	b
25	1PL	5-3/4" x 3/4"	14.66	1' 3-3/4"	1.34	20	b
26	1B	1-1/2" x 3/4"	3.83	3-1/2"	0.30	12	b
27	1B	1" x 3/4"	2.55	1' 5-3/4"	1.50	5	b

Total weight per base: 752 lb.

Fig. 11-2. Bill of material.

The same procedure is followed for each item. "Rd" and "B" are abbreviations for "round" and "bar," respectively. The weights of the rolled sections are listed in warehouse stock lists. Item 3 specifies a plate 2¼ in. thick, which carries a size extra of $0.30 per hundred. The total weight of steel in one base adds up to 752 lb.

Steel warehouses publish pamphlets listing extras, deductions, quantity differentials, and standard tolerances in thickness, width, and length for various rolled sections. Variations from true flatness and extras for special flatness are stated. The designer should be familiar with these data in order that he may use the cheapest material and still get the proper steel for the job.

TABLE 11–1[1]

POUNDS OF ELECTRODE REQUIRED PER FOOT OF WELD

Size, In.	Plain butt welds 50% penetration	Fillet welds	Vee welds	Types*
3/32		0.048		
1/8		0.080		
5/32		0.012		
3/16	0.08	0.15	0.16	60° vee
1/4	0.133	0.20	0.36	60° vee
5/16		0.29	0.48	60° vee
3/8	0.226	0.40	0.58	60° vee
1/2	0.46	0.75	1.00	60° vee or double vee
5/8		1.30	1.70	60° vee
3/4		2.10	1.90	Single U or double vee
1		3.20	2.40	Single U or double vee
1 1/8			2.80	Double U or double vee
1 1/4			3.00	Double U or double vee
1 1/2			3.30	Double U
2			4.50	Double U
4			9.00	Double U

* In all cases, the designer should specify the type of vee most economical for a particular size of plate. The quantities shown above have been selected on this basis.

[1] References: (1) *A.W.S. Welding Handbook,* American Welding Society, New York, 1942 ed.; (2) *Procedure Handbook of Arc Welding Design and Practice,* 8th ed., The Lincoln Electric Co., Cleveland, 1945; (3) *The Welding Encyclopedia,* 11th ed., McGraw-Hill Book Company, Inc., New York, 1943.

THE REX WELDING CO.

220 King Ave.

Philadelphia, Pa.

Subject: **Estimate**	Date: Dec. 10, 1949

For: The Moon Machine Co.
         410 South St.
         Philadelphia, Pa.
	Drawing No.: 200-G
	Fig. by: E.A.W.

Buyer: Dwight Jenkins, P.A.	Chk'd by: T.S.G.

Required: 50 Weldments, Drawing No. 200-G.

Item	Weld 50 units.	
1	3/8 vee	2 x 27"
2	1/4F	2(2 x 20") + 2(2 x 2.36')
3	3/8 vee	4(8")
4	1/4F	4(1' + 16")
5	1/4F	2 x 3"
6	1/4F	2 x 16"
7	1/4F	1.67' + 1'
8	1/4F	2(40" + 2 x 2.36')
9	1/4F	28" + 4 x 1.67')
10	1/4F	4 x 20" + 4 x 1.83'
11	1/4F	4 x 20" + 4 x 2'
12	1/4F	2 x 1'
13	1/4F	4 x 8" + 2 x 1.67'
14	1/4F	3(18" + 1.21')
15	3/8F	10"
16	3/8F	5 + 7"
17	1/4F	3 x 10"
18	1/4F	10"
19	1/4F	13" + 7"
20	1/4F	9" + 13"
21	1/4F	7"
22	1/4F	11" + 2.6'
23	1/4F	7" + 1'
24	1/4F	10" + 4.6'
25	1/4F	1' + 2.68'
26	1/4F	3" + 7"
27	1/4F	2" + 3'

Totals: 1/4F: 123' at 0.2......... 24.6 lb
         3/8F: 2' at 0.4........... 0.8
         3/8 vee: 7.25' at 0.53....... `4.0
Weld rod weight per base: 29.4 lb

Fig. 11-3. Weld-rod estimate.

The next step in estimating is to determine the exact amount of welding rod required to fabricate the base. The summary is shown in Fig. 11–3. The estimator takes each steel item and determines the length of weld required to join this particular item to an adjacent item. For example, Item 1 and two ⅜-in. vee welds 27 in. long, which unite the four side plates. Item 2 is double-welded with ¼-in. fillet welds on all sides, the amount of welding being 2(2 × 20″) plus 2(2 × 2.36′). At the bottom, the total lengths of fillet and vee welds are multiplied by the pounds of weld rod per foot of respective type of weld. The total, 29.4 lb., is the amount of weld rod required to weld one base. This method of determining the amount of weld rod is highly accurate, since the lengths are taken directly from the drawing, and the figures for the amount of weld rod per foot of weld are based on actual consumption in production (see Table 11–1 on electrode consumption rates). Allowance is made in the unit figure for the stub-end losses. It is good practice to increase this estimated amount of weld rod by 5 to 10 per cent to take care of variations in the size of the weld.

A similar analysis is prepared for flame cutting. Each item is listed as shown in Fig. 11–4.

Item 1, when totaled, shows 18 ft. 4 in. of flame cutting in ⅜-in. plate. The cutting for each item is recorded, and at the bottom the total in feet for each plate thickness is multiplied by the cost of cutting per foot. The ⅜-in. vee welds, totaling 7.25 ft., are added to the ⅜-in.-plate total. These costs shown for flame cutting are standard warehouse costs as listed in a warehouse stock list and include both labor and gas. The total cost of burning for each base is shown at the bottom as $4.45.

The final estimate is shown in Fig. 11–5. The following materials enter into the work of fabricating 50 weldments: 752 lb. × 50 gives 37,600 lb. total gross weight of steel used. This figure is increased 5 per cent to allow for possible oversize variations in the weight of the plate and bar items. Plates and bars are sold to the warehouse by weight. The corrected amount of steel is multiplied by the cost of steel per hundredweight to give the total cost of the steel.

On the next line, the size extras are $0.20 × 50, totaling $10 for the 50 bases. The cost of paint is taken at $2 per ton of steel, and the total amount of weld rod at 1600 lb., which allows about

THE REX WELDING CO.
220 King Ave.
Philadelphia, Pa.

Subject: **Estimate**   Date: Dec. 10, 1949

For: The Moon Machine Co.
       410 South St.   Drawing No.:   200-G
       Philadelphia, Pa.   Fig. by: E.A.W.

Buyer: Dwight Jenkins, P.A.   Chk'd by: T.S.G.

Required: 50 Weldments, Drawing No. 200-G.

Item	Flame cut 50 units.	
1	3/8"	11" + 2.6' + 64" + 29" + 20" + 3' + 30"
2	-----	
3	2-1/4"	4(8")
4	-----	
5	1-1/2"	2(7-1/2")
6	-----	
7	-----	
8	3/8"	14" + 9" + 14" + 5" + 10"
9	-----	
10	3/8"	15"
11	3/8"	4'
12	-----	
13	3/8"	18" + 20" + 1'
14	3/8"	2(1')
15	-----	
16	-----	
17	-----	
18	-----	
19	-----	
20	-----	
21	-----	
22	3/4"	6" + 1.3' + 11" + 4"
23	1/2"	10" + 13"
24	3/4"	10" + 4.6' + 14" + 5"
25	3/4"	11" + 1.3' + 14" + 20"
26	-----	
27	-----	

```
Totals:    3/8":  35' at 0.055.......  $1.93
           1/2":  2.1' at 0.07.......   0.25
           3/4":  16' at 0.085.......   1.36
         1-1/2":  1.25 at 0.15.......   0.25
         2-1/4":  3' at 0.22.........   0.66
   Cost of flame cutting:             $4.45
```

Fig. 11-4. Flame-cutting estimate.

THE REX WELDING CO.
220 King Ave.
Philadelphia, Pa.

Subject: Estimate   Date: Dec. 10, 1949

For: The Moon Machine Co.
       410 South St.   Drawing No.: 200-G
       Philadelphia, Pa.   Fig. by: E.A.W.

Buyer: Dwight Jenkins, P.A.   Chk'd by: T.S.G.

Required: 50 Weldments, Drawing No. 200-G.

```
Material: 752 lb x 50 = 37,600 lb.
   Plus 5% = 39,480 lb at steel price cwt... $
   Size extras: $0.20 x 50..................      10.00
   Paint: 20 tons at $2.00..................      40.00
   Weld rod: 1600 lb at $0.08...............     128.00
      Total cost of materials............... $

Shop labor................................... $2Q50.00
Shop overhead...............................

Stress relief...............................     350.00
Sandblasting................................     350.00

Cartage.....................................      50.00
      Total manufacturing cost............. $

Profit, administration, and selling........
      Total selling price.................. $
```

```
Shop costs:
   Templates.................. $  20.00
   Layout.....................    180.00
   Shearing and saw cutting...    100.00
   Bending....................    125.00
   Flame cutting..............    225.00
   Welding....................    600.00
   Fit-up.....................    500.00
   Grinding and cleaning......    200.00
   Painting...................    100.00
      Total shop labor........ $2050.00
```

Fig. 11-5. Final estimate.

6 per cent over the estimated amount. Most of the welding of these bases will be made with ¼-in. electrodes, for which the price of $0.08 per pound is used. The column of material costs is then totaled.

The shop costs are summarized at the bottom left. The cost of preparing the cardboard templates for flame cutting and bending is estimated at $20, and the layout work, including laying out pieces for shearing, flame cutting, sawing, and other operations, is estimated to a $180 total. Shearing and saw cutting total $100. The burning and welding costs are only slightly increased above the calculated amount.

A welding operator working on large heavy bases with long continuous seams melts electrode metal at a maximum all-day rate of 5 lb. per hour. This figure has been arrived at from experience and represents a welding efficiency of about 50 per cent, with allowances made for changing electrodes, shifting the work, setting up, and other nonproductive operations. At the other extreme is the small base with short welds and numerous changes in position, for which the melting rate may be as low as 1 lb. per hour. For this particular base, it is estimated that the welder will melt slightly under 2.5 lb. per hour and will require a welding time of 12 hr. per base. The men who work along with the welder in fitting up and aligning the parts will require a total of about five-sixths of the welder's time. Each weldment should require 4 hr. for cleaning off the loose oxide and scale and grinding the vee welds flush with the wall plates. Painting is estimated to require 4.5 hr. per ton.

Below "Total cost of materials," the following items are added: shop labor, shop overhead, stress relief, sandblasting, and cartage. The total of all items down to this point gives the total manufacturing cost. To this total must be added profit, administration, and selling cost, giving the total lot selling price.

Stress Design Data

A. BEAM-DEFLECTION EQUATIONS

$$d_x = \frac{Px^2}{6\,EI}(3\,L - x)$$

$$d_{max} = \frac{PL^3}{3\,EI}$$

$$d_x = \frac{Px^2}{6\,EI}(3\,a - x) \text{ for } 0 < x < a$$

$$d_x = \frac{Pa^2}{6\,EI}(3\,x - a) \text{ for } a < x < L$$

$$d_{max} = \frac{Pa^2}{6\,EI}(3\,L - a)$$

$$d_x = \frac{wx^2}{24\,EI}(x^2 + 6\,L^2 - 4\,Lx)$$

$$d_{max} = \frac{wL^4}{8\,EI}$$

$$d_x = \frac{wx^2}{120\,LEI}(10\,L^3 - 10\,L^2x + 5\,Lx^2 - x^3)$$

$$d_{max} = \frac{wL^4}{30\,EI}$$

$$d_{x_1} = \frac{wb^3}{12\,EI}(2\,a - 2\,x_1 + b)$$

$$d_{x_2} = \frac{wx_2^3}{4\,EI} + \frac{wb^2(b - x_2)^2}{6\,EI} + \frac{w(b - x_2)^4}{8\,EI}$$

$$d_{max} = \frac{wb^3}{24\,EI}(3\,b + 4\,a)$$

188

A. BEAM-DEFLECTION EQUATIONS (Cont.)

$$d_{x_1} = \frac{wx_1^2(a-x_1)^2}{4EI} + \frac{wx_1(a-x_1)^3}{3EI} + \frac{w(a-x_1)^4}{8EI}$$
$$+ \frac{wab}{EI}\left(\frac{a^2}{2} - \frac{ax_1}{2} + \frac{3ab}{4} - \frac{bx_1}{2} + \frac{b^2}{3}\right)$$

$$d_{x_2} = \frac{wa^2}{4EI}(b-x_2)^2 + \frac{wax_2(b-x_2)^2}{2EI} + \frac{wa(b-x_2)^3}{3EI}$$

$$d_{max} = \frac{wa}{EI}\left(\frac{a^3}{8} + \frac{a^2b}{2}\right.$$
$$\left. + \frac{3ab^2}{4} + \frac{b^3}{3}\right)$$

$$d_x = \frac{Mx^2}{2EI}$$

$$d_{max} = \frac{ML^2}{2EI}$$

$$d_x = \frac{Px}{12EI}\left(\frac{3L^2}{4} - x^2\right) \text{ for } 0 < x < \frac{L}{2}$$

$$d_{max} = \frac{PL^3}{48EI}$$

To left of Load P
$$d_x = \frac{Pbx}{6LEI}(L^2 - x^2 - b^2)$$

To right of Load P
$$d_x = \frac{Pb}{6LEI}\left[\frac{L}{b}(x-a)^3 + (L^2 - b^2)x - x^3\right]$$

$$d_{max} = \frac{Pb(L^2 - b^2)^{\frac{3}{2}}}{9\sqrt{3}\,LEI}$$
$$\text{at } x = \sqrt{\frac{L^2 - b^2}{3}}$$

At center if $a > b$
$$d_c = \frac{Pb}{48EI}(3L^2 - 4b^2)$$

A. BEAM-DEFLECTION EQUATIONS (*Cont.*)

	$$d_x = \frac{wx}{24\,EI}\left(L^3 - 2\,Lx^2 + x^3\right)$$	$$d_{\max} = \frac{5\,wL^4}{384\,EI}$$
	$$d_x = \frac{MLx}{6\,EI}\left(1 - \frac{x^2}{L^2}\right)$$	$$d_{\max} = \frac{ML^2}{9\sqrt{3}\,EI}$$ at $x = \dfrac{L}{\sqrt{3}}$ at center $$d_c = \frac{ML^2}{16\,EI}$$
	$$dx = \frac{Mx}{6\,LEI}\left(L - x\right)\left(2\,L - x\right)$$	$$d_{\max} = \frac{ML^2}{9\sqrt{3}\,EI}$$ at $x = \left(1 - \dfrac{1}{\sqrt{3}}\right)L$ at center $$d_c = \frac{ML^2}{16\,EI}$$

190

A. BEAM-DEFLECTION EQUATIONS (*Cont.*)

$$d_x = \frac{3}{32}\frac{PL^2x}{EI} - \frac{Px^3}{6EI} \text{ for } 0 < x < \frac{L}{4}$$

$$d_x = \frac{PL^2x}{16EI} + \frac{PL^3}{192EI} + \frac{PL}{8EI}\left(x - \frac{L}{4}\right)^2$$

$$\text{for } \frac{L}{4} < x < \frac{3}{4}L$$

$$d_{\max} = \frac{11}{384}\frac{PL^3}{EI}$$

$$d_x = \frac{Px}{3EI}\left(\frac{L^2}{3} - \frac{x^2}{2}\right) \text{ for } 0 < x < \frac{L}{3}$$

$$d_x = \frac{PL^2x}{18EI} + \frac{PL^3}{81EI} - \frac{PL}{6EI}\left(x - \frac{L}{3}\right)^2$$

$$\text{for } \frac{L}{3} < x < \frac{2L}{3}$$

$$d_{\max} = \frac{23}{648}\frac{PL^3}{EI}$$

191

B. STANDARD PROPORTIONS OF GROOVES FOR FUSION WELDS

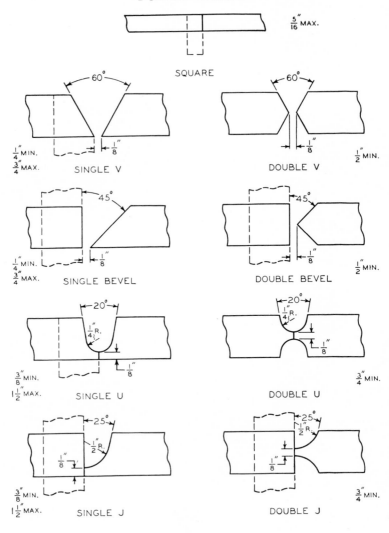

$\frac{5}{16}''$ MAX.

SQUARE

SINGLE V

DOUBLE V

SINGLE BEVEL

DOUBLE BEVEL

SINGLE U

DOUBLE U

SINGLE J

DOUBLE J

C. MINIMUM-SIZE FILLET WELDS FOR DIFFERENT THICKNESSES OF PLATE

Plate Thickness, In.	*Minimum Weld Size, In.*
$\frac{1}{8}$ to $\frac{3}{16}$, inclusive	$\frac{1}{8}$
$\frac{1}{4}$ to $\frac{5}{16}$, inclusive	$\frac{3}{16}$
$\frac{3}{8}$ to $\frac{5}{8}$, inclusive	$\frac{1}{4}$
$\frac{3}{4}$ to 1, inclusive	$\frac{3}{8}$
$1\frac{1}{8}$ to $1\frac{3}{8}$, inclusive	$\frac{1}{2}$
Above $1\frac{1}{2}$	$\frac{3}{4}$

D. WELD STRESSES—METHOD OF FIGURING

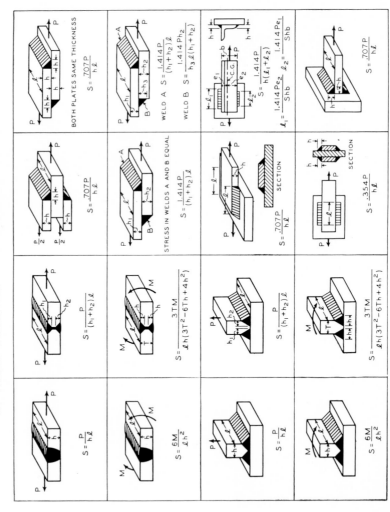

D. WELD STRESSES—METHOD OF FIGURING (*Cont.*)

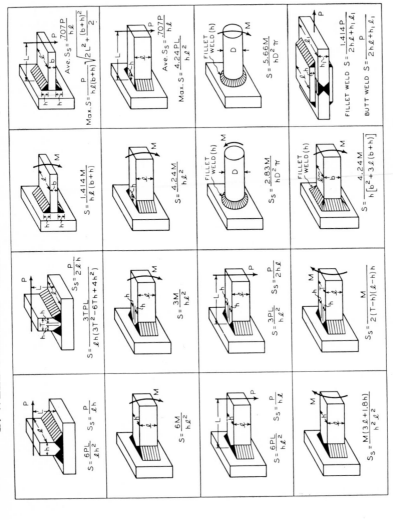

E. ALLOWABLE ECCENTRIC LONGITUDINAL
LOADS ON FILLET WELDS

$$\frac{P}{W} = \frac{9.6L}{\sqrt{1+\left(\frac{6a}{L}\right)^2}}$$

Long. load $= P$ (kips)
Weld size $= W$ (in.)
Eccentricity $= a$ (in.)

Table gives $\dfrac{P}{W}$ (kips)

P (in kips) $= W \times$ value in table
Unit stress on welds $= 13,600$ p.s.i.

a, in. \ L, in.	2	4	6	8	10	12	14	16	18	20
0	19	38	57	76	96	115	134	153	172	192
¼	15	36	56	75	95	114	133	153	172	192
½	10	30	51	71	91	111	131	151	170	190
¾	7	25	46	66	87	107	128	148	167	187
1	....	21	41	61	82	102	123	143	163	183
1¼	....	18	36	56	76	97	118	138	158	179
1½	....	15	32	51	71	92	113	133	154	174
1¾	....	13	28	46	66	86	107	128	149	170
2	....	....	25	42	61	81	102	123	144	164
2½	....	....	21	36	53	72	92	112	133	153
3	....	....	18	31	46	64	82	101	122	142
3½	....	....	16	27	41	57	74	93	112	132
4	....	....	....	24	37	51	68	85	103	122
4½	....	....	....	21	33	47	61	77	95	114
5	....	....	....	19	30	42	57	72	88	106
5½	....	....	....	18	28	39	52	67	82	99
6	....	....	....	....	25	36	49	62	77	93

Example: Assume $P = 30$ kips, $a = 3$ in., and that a ⁵⁄₁₆-in. fillet weld will be used. P divided by weld size $= 30$ divided by ⁵⁄₁₆ $= 96$. Opposite $a = 3$ in the table, we find that the number next larger than 96 is 101, under $L = 16$ in., which is the length required to support the load. If two welds are used, double the values given in the table.

F. ALLOWABLE ECCENTRIC TRANSVERSE LOADS ON FILLET WELDS

$$\frac{P}{W} = \frac{9.6 L}{1 + \frac{6a}{L}}$$

Trans. load $= P$ (kips)
Weld size $= W$ (in.)
Eccentricity $= a$ (in.)

Table gives $\frac{P}{W}$ (kips)

P (in kips) $= W \times$ value in table
Unit stress on welds $= 13,600$ p.s.i.

a, in. \ L, in.	2	4	6	8	10	12	14	16	18	20
0	19	38	57	76	96	115	134	153	172	192
1/4	11	27	46	64	83	102	121	140	159	178
1/2	7	21	38	56	74	92	110	129	148	167
3/4	....	18	33	49	66	83	101	120	138	156
1	....	15	29	44	60	76	94	111	129	147
1 1/4	....	....	25	39	55	70	87	104	122	139
1 1/2	....	....	23	36	50	66	81	98	115	132
1 3/4	....	....	....	33	47	61	76	92	109	125
2	....	....	....	30	43	57	72	87	103	120
2 1/2	....	....	....	....	38	51	65	79	94	109
3	....	....	....	....	34	46	58	72	86	101
3 1/2	....	....	....	....	....	41	53	66	79	93
4	....	....	....	....	....	38	49	61	74	87
4 1/2	....	....	....	....	....	35	45	57	69	81
5	....	....	....	....	....	....	42	53	64	76

Example: Assume $P = 30$ kips, $a = 3$ in., and that a 5/16-in. fillet weld will be used. P divided by weld size $= 30$ divided by 5/16 $= 96$. Opposite $a = 3$ in the table, we find that the number next larger than 96 is 101, under $L = 20$ in. which is the length of weld required to support the load. If two welds are used, double the values given in the table.

G. FLEXIBLE-TYPE BEAM SEATS —
ALLOWABLE LOADS ON OUTSTANDING LEGS

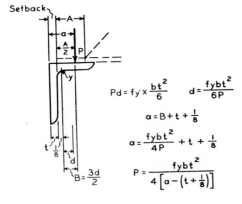

$$Pd = fy \times \frac{bt^2}{6} \qquad d = \frac{fybt^2}{6P}$$

$$a = B + t + \frac{1}{8}$$

$$a = \frac{fybt^2}{4P} + t + \frac{1}{8}$$

$$P = \frac{fybt^2}{4\left[a - \left(t + \frac{1}{8}\right)\right]}$$

A is the minimum length of bearing required to distribute the beam reaction into its web without crushing or buckling.

$$a = \frac{A}{2} + \text{setback.}$$

fy = yield point stress at point y (33,000 lb. p. s. i.)
$b = 1$ in.

t, in. a, in.	$\frac{3}{8}$	$\frac{7}{16}$	$\frac{1}{2}$	$\frac{9}{16}$	$\frac{5}{8}$	$\frac{11}{16}$	$\frac{3}{4}$	$\frac{13}{16}$	$\frac{7}{8}$	$\frac{15}{16}$	1
1	2.32	3.61	5.50	...	...	...	...	...	...	...	...
1¼	1.54	2.30	3.30	4.64	...	...	...	...	...	...	...
1½	1.16	1.68	2.35	3.22	4.29	5.67	...	...	...	...	...
1¾	0.92	1.33	1.83	2.46	3.22	4.16	5.30	...	...	...	...
2	...	1.10	1.50	1.99	2.57	3.28	4.13	5.13	...	...	...
2¼	...	0.94	1.27	1.67	2.14	2.71	3.37	4.15	5.05	6.10	...
2½	...	...	1.10	1.44	1.84	2.31	2.85	3.49	4.21	5.04	6.00
2¾	...	...	0.97	1.27	1.61	2.01	2.47	3.01	3.61	4.29	5.07
3	...	...	...	1.13	1.43	1.78	2.18	2.64	3.15	3.74	4.40

Note: The maximum effective length of a seat angle shall not be considered greater than the width of the beam flange plus 6 in. For proper clearance of shop welds, the minimum length of a seat angle should not be less than the width of the beam flange plus 2 in.

For an example, see Table H on page 199.

H. FLEXIBLE-TYPE BEAM SEATS—
ALLOWABLE LOADS ON VERTICAL LEGS

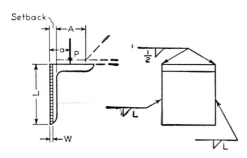

$$\frac{P}{W} = \frac{2 \times 9.6 \times L}{\sqrt{1 + \frac{(6a)}{L}^2}}$$

Load $= P$ (kips)
Weld size $= W$ (in.)
Moment arm $= a$ (in.)

Table gives $\frac{P}{W}$ in kips

P (in kips) $=$
$W \times$ value in table
Unit stress on welds $=$
13,600 p.s.i.

$$\frac{P}{W} = \frac{2 \times 9.6 \times L}{\sqrt{1 + \left(\frac{6a}{L}\right)^2}}$$

a, in. \ L, in.	4	5	6	7	8
1	42	61	81	102	122
$1\frac{1}{4}$	36	53	72	91	112
$1\frac{1}{2}$	31	46	64	82	102
$1\frac{3}{4}$	27	41	57	74	93
2	24	37	51	67	85
$2\frac{1}{4}$	21	33	46	62	78
$2\frac{1}{2}$	19	30	42	57	72
$2\frac{3}{4}$	18	27	39	52	67
3	16	25	36	48	62

Example: Assume 16 CB 40 with end reaction of 21 kips. $A = 1.84$ for web crushing. $A = 1.53$ for web buckling. With a setback of $\frac{1}{2}$ in., $a = 1.42$. Use $a = 1\frac{1}{2}$. Flange width $= 7$ in. Minimum length of seat $= 7 + 2 = 9$ in. $21 + 9 = 2.33$ kips per linear inch. From Table F on page 197 we find that a $\frac{1}{2}$-in. seat angle is required. Using $\frac{3}{8}$-in. welds, $21 \div \frac{3}{8} = 56$. From the above table we find that the vertical leg of the seat angle $= 6$ in.
Required angle $= 6 \times 3\frac{1}{2} \times \frac{1}{2} \times 9$.

I. PLATE GIRDERS

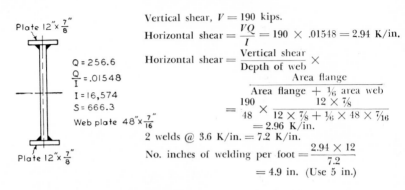

Plate 12″ x $\frac{7}{8}$″

$Q = 256.6$

$\frac{Q}{I} = .01548$

$I = 16,574$

$S = 666.3$

Web plate 48″x $\frac{7}{16}$″

Plate 12″x $\frac{7}{8}$″

Vertical shear, $V = 190$ kips.

Horizontal shear $= \dfrac{VQ}{I} = 190 \times .01548 = 2.94$ K/in.

Horizontal shear $= \dfrac{\text{Vertical shear}}{\text{Depth of web}} \times$

$\dfrac{\text{Area flange}}{\text{Area flange} + \frac{1}{6} \text{ area web}}$

$= \dfrac{190}{48} \times \dfrac{12 \times \frac{7}{8}}{12 \times \frac{7}{8} + \frac{1}{6} \times 48 \times \frac{7}{16}}$

$= 2.96$ K/in.

2 welds @ 3.6 K/in. $= 7.2$ K/in.

No. inches of welding per foot $= \dfrac{2.94 \times 12}{7.2}$

$= 4.9$ in. (Use 5 in.)

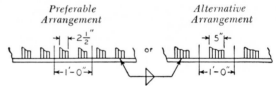

Preferable
Arrangement

Alternative
Arrangement

$Q =$ statical moment of flange $= 12 \times \frac{7}{8} \times 24\frac{7}{16} = 256.6$ in.^{3}

Calculation of pitch of welds connecting flange to web.

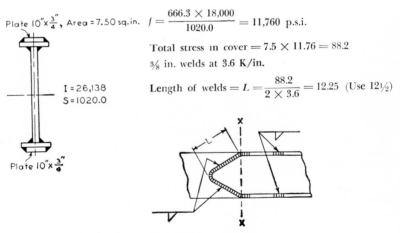

Plate 10″x$\frac{3}{4}$″, Area = 7.50 sq.in.

$I = 26,138$

$S = 1020.0$

Plate 10″x$\frac{3}{4}$″

$f = \dfrac{666.3 \times 18,000}{1020.0} = 11,760$ p.s.i.

Total stress in cover $= 7.5 \times 11.76 = 88.2$

$\frac{3}{8}$ in. welds at 3.6 K/in.

Length of welds $= L = \dfrac{88.2}{2 \times 3.6} = 12.25$ (Use $12\frac{1}{2}$)

Calculation of cover plate welds.

J. BEAM BRACKETS

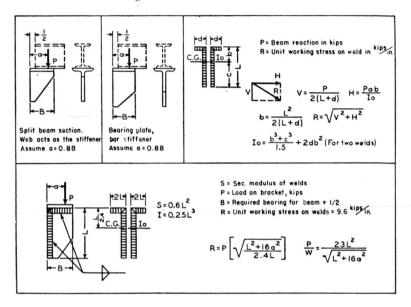

B, in.	a, in.	L, in. 8	10	12	14	16	18	20	22	24	26	28	30
$2\frac{1}{2}$	2.0	130	179	229	279	329	378	427	475	523	571	619	666
3	2.4	117	166	215	265	315	365	414	463	512	561	609	657
$3\frac{1}{2}$	2.8	107	153	201	251	301	351	401	451	500	549	598	646
4	3.2	97	141	188	237	287	337	387	437	487	536	585	635
$4\frac{1}{2}$	3.6	89	131	176	224	273	323	373	423	473	523	572	622
$5\frac{1}{2}$	4.4	76	113	155	200	247	296	345	395	445	495	545	595
$6\frac{1}{2}$	5.2	66	99	138	179	224	271	318	367	416	467	516	567

Example: Assume $P = 100$ kips, $B = 4$, and that a $\frac{5}{16}$-in. fillet weld will be used. P divided by weld size $= 100$ divided by $\frac{5}{16} = 320$. Opposite $B = 4$ in. we find that the number next larger than 320 is 337, under $L = 18$ in., which is the length of bracket required.

The analysis of this type of connection assumes that the beam's deflection causes its resultant reaction to act at a distance $a = 0.8B$ from the face of the supporting member.

In order to attain a proper amount of weld along the bracket's vertical leg, the length of each horizontal weld connecting the bracket to its support should not exceed 20 per cent of the length of the vertical weld.

K. WELDED CONNECTIONS ON
BOTH SIDES OF A BEAM WEB

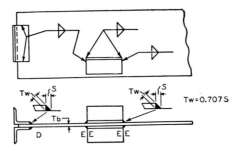

Fw = allowable shear on weld throat = 13,600 p.s.i.
Fb = allowable shear on beam web = 15,000 p.s.i.

END CONNECTION	INTERIOR CONNECTIONS (*Opposite*)
Shear in welds must not exceed shear in web at D. $$2 \times Tw \times Fw \gtreqless Fb \times Tb$$ $$2 \times 13,600 \times Tw \gtreqless 15,000 \times Tb$$ $$Tw \gtreqless \frac{15,000}{2 \times 13,600} \times Tb$$ $$0.707S \gtreqless \frac{15,000}{2 \times 13,600} \times Tb$$ $$S \gtreqless \frac{15,000}{1.414 \times 13,600} \times Tb$$ $$S \gtreqless 0.78\,Tb$$ $$S \gtreqless \tfrac{3}{4}Tb$$	Shear in welds must not exceed shears in web at E-E. $$2 \times Tw \times Fw \gtreqless 2 \times Fb \times Tb$$ $$2 \times 13,600 \times Tw \gtreqless 2 \times Fb \times Tb$$ $$Tw \gtreqless \frac{Fb}{13,600} \times Tb$$ $$0.707S \gtreqless \frac{Fb}{13,600} \times Tb$$ $$S \gtreqless \frac{Fb}{9600} \times Tb$$
The strength of end connections having welds larger than three fourths of the web thickness is governed by the strength of the web.	Fb, the allowable shear on the beam web, must be reduced by the amount of shear, in pounds per square inch, which has been accumulated in the beam web up to the point of application of the load.

Bibliography

MAGAZINE ARTICLES

Allen, T. W., "Taylor-Winfield Fabricating Plant Specialized in Welded Machine Frames," *Welding Engineer,* Vol. 24, No. 9 (September 1939).

Austin, A. S., "Yardstick For Buying Welded Machine Parts," *Machinery,* Vol. 39, No. 6 (February 1933).

Bedell, A. E., and T. G. Morrison, "Intricate Machine Parts," *Steel,* Vol. 114, No. 26 (June 1944).

———, and J. B. Quigley, "Why Stress Relieve?", *Welding Engineer,* Vol. 29, No. 4 (April 1944).

Benson, J. E., and H. Allison, "Low Temperature Annealing of Welded Mild Steel Structures to Relieve Internal Stresses," *Iron and Steel Institute, Symposium on the Welding of Iron and Steel,* Vol. 2 (1935).

Bibber, L. C., "The Theory of Stresses in Welds," *Welding Journal,* Vol. 9, No. 4 (April 1930).

Birkle, H., "Calculation of Box-type Machinery Frames Restricted against Deformation," *Engineers Digest,* Vol. 4, No. 2 (February 1943).

Boardman, H. C., "Stresses in Welded Structures," *Welding Journal,* Vol. 24, No. 1 (January 1945).

Bolz, R. W., "Production Processes—Their Influence on Design," *Machine Design,* Vol. 18, No. 12 (June 1946).

Boom, W. B., "Fabricate Machine Bases by Welding Steel Plates," *Iron Trade Review,* Vol. 83, No. 3 (July 1928).

Booth, T. H., "Machine Tool Fabricated by Welding," *Welding,* Vol. 1, No. 5 (March 1930).

Braithwaite, R. G., "Application of Welding to Steel Structures," *Inst. Welding Trans.,* Vol. 8, No. 2 (May 1945).

Brinton, C. C., "Development In Welding Large Structures," *Mechanical Engineering,* Vol. 60, No. 1 (January 1938).

———, "Prominent Fabricator Reviews Work in Welding Large Structures," *Welding Engineer,* Vol. 22, No. 11 (November 1937).

Brooking, W. J., "Machining of Arc Welded Products," *Iron Age,* Vol. 152, No. 24 (December 1943).

———, "Bases for Machine Tool and Power Units Tailored to Fit by Welding," *Steel,* Vol. 109, No. 14 (October 1941).

Brown, C. O., "Equipment and Design," *Ind. and Eng. Chem.* 39: Supplement 81A–82A (August 1947).

Brown, J. L., "Designing Arc Welded Machine Bases," *Machinery,* Vol. 35, No. 7 (March 1929).

Brown, J. L., "Casting or Welding in Machine Design," *Trans. A.S.M.E.,* Vol. 58, No. 7 (October 1936).

Browne, L. E., "Welding in Steel Construction Work," *Steel,* Vol. 116, No. 13 (March 26, 1945).

Card, H. S., "Forming Steel Plate for Welded Fabrication," *Welding Engineer,* Vol. 24, No. 6 (June 1939).

——, "Machinery—Expanding Market for Welding," *Welding Engineer,* Vol. 24, No. 3 (March 1939).

Chapman, E., "Arc Welding in Machine Design," *Machinery* (London), Vol. 41, No. 1065 (March 1933).

——, "Arc Welding Introduces New Methods in Machine Design," *Machinery,* Vol. 39, No. 4 (December 1932).

——, "Design of Industrial Equipment in Welded Steel," *Iron and Steel Eng.,* Vol. 9, No. 4 (April 1932).

——, "Flexibility of Welding Combines Strength and Lightness," *Machine Design,* Vol. 4, No. 5 (May 1932).

——, "Welding Facilitates Use of Stiffest Shapes for Machine Tool Loads," *Iron Age,* Vol. 12, No. 17 (April 1932).

Charlton, E. J., "Trends in the Case of Welded Machinery Parts," *Machine Design,* Vol 17, No. 1 (January 1945).

——, "Trends in Use of Welded Machinery Parts," *Mechanical Engineering,* Vol. 67, No. 2 (February 1945).

Chase, H., "Fabrication of Machine Bases by Arc Welding Method," *Machinery* (London), Vol. 60, No. 6 (May 1942).

Coker, E. G., "Stress Analysis of Fusion Joints," *Iron and Steel Institute, Symposium on the Welding of Iron and Steel* (London), Vol. 2 (1935).

Cooper, J. H., "Design and Welding of Fabricated Machinery," *Iron Age,* Vol. 145, No. 23 (June 1940).

——, "Steel Plate Fabrication in Heavy Machinery Field," *Welding Journal,* Vol. 17, No. 2 (February 1938).

——, "Welded Machine Fabrication in Step with Styling," *Welding Engineer,* Vol. 22, No. 9 (September 1937).

Coyle, J. C., "Iron Works Products Made by Welding," *Welding,* Vol. 1, No. 8 (June 1930).

Davies, H. E., "Jigs and Fixtures for Welding," *Welding Journal,* Vol. 17, No. 4 (April 1938).

Davis, A. F., "The Application of Arc Welding in Production Manufacturing," *Welding Journal,* Vol. 8, No. 2 (February 1929).

——, "Why Use Rolled Steel for Machine Bases?", *Machinery,* Vol. 35, No. 8 (April 1929).

DeWitt, E. J., "Welding of Small Sub-assemblies in Program of All-Welded Machines," *Welding Journal,* Vol. 18, No. 1 (January 1939).

Dorey, S. F., "Welding as Substitute for Casting," *Institution of Engineers and Shipbuilders in Scotland, Trans.,* Vol. 83, Paper No. 1008 (March 1940). Also in *Foundry Trade Journal,* Vol. 62, No. 1228 (February 1940).

Dorret, J. A., "Modern Fabrication Technique," *Inst. Welding Trans.*, Vol. 8, No. 1 (February 1945).

———, "Some Modern Applications of Welding to Engineering," *Shipbuilder and Marine Engine Builder*, Vol. 52, No. 433 (April 1945).

Dubie, O. L.., "Jigs & Fixtures Facilitate Economic Mass Welding," *Steel*, Vol. 122, No. 18 (May 3, 1948).

Elberty, R. S., "Shape of Things to Come," *Machine Design*, Vol. 15, No. 8 (August 1943).

Gast, R. A., "Marked Economy of Welded Construction in Production of Machine Bases," *Machinery*, Vol. 49, No. 1 (September 1942).

———, "Analyze Jobs for Better Welds," *American Machinist*, Vol. 85, No. 21 (October 15, 1941).

Gibson, A. E., "Welding and Steel Industry," *Iron and Steel Eng.*, Vol. 19, No. 2 (February 1934).

Gillen, G. M., "Profiles for Propellers," *Welding Journal*, Vol. 15, No. 6 (June 1936).

Griffith, J. R., "Effect of Fillet Welds on Eccentricity," *Welding*, Vol. 4, No. 1 (January 1933).

Heaps, T. P., and S. C. McDowell, "Formulas and Tables for Determining Length of Parts before Bending," *Machinery*, Vol. 45, No. 6 (February 1939).

Helmkamp, R. F., "Automatic Oxyacetylene Operations," *Welding Journal*, Vol. 26, No. 5 (May 1947).

Herbst, H. T., "Production Applications for Inert Gas Shielded Arc Welding," *Welding Journal*, Vol. 26, No. 5 (May 1947).

Herrick, C. B., "Importance of Producing Welds of Specified Size," *Industry and Welding*, Vol. 16, No. 12 (December 1943).

Hill, H. V., "Development in Design of Welded Steel Structure," *Structural Eng.*, Vol. 23, No. 8 (August 1945).

Hoogaard, W., "Stress Distribution in Longitudinal Welds and Adjoining Structures," *Journal of Mathematics and Physics*, Vol. 13, No. 5 (May 1934).

Jacobs, F. B., "Welding Operations Aid in Production of Machine Tools," *Welding Engineer*, Vol. 20, No. 12 (December 1935).

Jaeger, A., "A Review of Stresses in Welded Joints," *Here's How It's Welded*, Vol. 2, No. 1 (January 1934).

Jefferson, T. B., "Design for Arc Welding," *Welding Engineer*, Vol. 29, No. 9 (September 1944).

Jensen, C. D., "Combined Stresses in Fillet Welds," *Welding Journal*, Vol. 13, No. 2 (February 1934).

Jennings, C. H., "The Relief of Welding Strains by Annealing," *Welding Journal*, Vol. 10, No. 9 (September 1931).

———, "Welding Design," *Trans. A.S.M.E.*, Vol. 58, No. 7 (October 1936).

Johansson, G., "Welded Structures," *Product Eng.*, Vol. 13, No. 7 (July 1942).

Johnston, T., "Designing Welded Steel Machine Bases," *Industry and Welding*, Vol. 3, No. 5 (November 1933).

——, "Fabrication of Machine Parts by Welding," *Welding Journal*, Vol. 16, No. 6 (June 1937).

——, "Machine Base Construction," *Industry and Welding*, Vol. 10, No. 8 (August 1937).

Jones, O. C., "Economical Fabrication," *Welding Journal*, Vol. 15, No. 9 (September 1936).

Kemeny, A. A., "Principles of Machine Design," *Canadian Machinery*, Vol. 55, No. 6 (January 1945).

Kerry, F. G., "Precision Oxyacetylene Cutting," *Canadian Metals and Metal Industries*, Vol. 8, No. 12 (December 1945).

Kinkead, R. E., "When Should Welding Be Employed in Machine Design," *Machine Design*, Vol. 1, No. 1 (September 1929).

——, "Over Horizon," *Machine Design*, Vol. 8, No. 10 (October 1936).

Koenigsberger, F., "The Rigidity of Machine Tool Beds," *Machinery* (London), Vol. 52, No. 1339 (June 9, 1938).

——, "Must a Rigid Machine Tool Be Heavy?", *Machinery* (London), Vol. 56, No. 1436 (April 1940).

——, "Design and Construction of Machine Tool Parts in Fabricated Steel," *Machinery* (London), Vol. 58, No. 1491 (May 1941).

——, "Application of Welding in the Design of Machine Tools," *Welding*, Vol. 10, No. 4, May–June 1942.

——, "Redesign of Cast Iron Machine Parts for Welded Construction," *Welder*, Vol. 12, No. 81 (January-June 1942).

——, "Machine Design for Fabricated Welded Construction," *Machinery* (London), Vol. 62, No. 1589 (March 1943).

——, "Application of Fabricated Construction to Machine Design," *Engineer*, Vol. 177, No. 4608 (May 1944).

Kugler, A. N., "Welding Jigs and Fixtures," *Welding Journal*, Vol. 24, No. 1 (January 1945).

Landis, G. G., "Unusual Machine Tools Built by Welding," *Machinery*, Vol. 45, No. 4 (December 1938).

Lincoln, J. F., "Redesign for Production Welding," *Iron Age*, Vol. 123, No. 11 (March 15, 1929).

Lindemuth, F. L., and C. A. Wills, "Overcoming Problems Encountered in Welding Heavy Machinery," *Canadian Machinery*, Vol. 49, No. 1 (January 1937).

——, and ——, "Welding Heavy Machinery," *Welding Journal*, Vol. 15, No. 10 (October 1936).

Luehrs, D. M., "Building Machines of Welded Steel," *Iron Age*, Vol. 124, No. 5 (August 1929).

Marsh, H. G., "Use of Rolled Steel in Machine Construction," American Iron and Steel Inst., 1933.

——, "Rolled Steel in Machine Construction," *A.S.M.E. Trans.*, Vol. 58,

No. 7 (October 1936). Also in *Machine Design*, Vol. 8, No. 10 (October 1936).

McQuail, H. W., "Needed—Better Teamwork between Designer and Metallurgist," *Machine Design*, Vol. 16, No. 10 (October 1944).

Mikulak, J., "Design of Welded Machinery," *Welding Journal*, Vol. 24, No. 1 (January 1945).

Moore, E. C., "Design and Cost of Welded Machine Structure," *Inst. Welding Trans.*, Vol. 3, No. 1 (January 1940).

Murdock, M. L., "Base Plates of Welded Steel," *Iron Age*, Vol. 148, No. 21 (November 1941).

Nacin, R. A., "Jigs and Manipulators Expedite Heavy Welding," *Commonwealth Engineer*, Vol. 35, No. 4 (November 1, 1947).

Nenninger, L. F., and W. A. Maddox, "Recent Developments in Welding of Machine Tools," *Welding Journal*, Vol. 17, No. 10 (October 1938).

————, and ————, "Recent Developments in Welding Various Units for Machine Tool Construction," *Canadian Machinery*, Vol. 15, No. 8 (August 1940).

Oberg, E., "Influence of Welding on Machine Design and Shop Practice," *Machinery*, Vol. 43, Nos. 4 and 5 (December 1936).

Ode, K. F., "Commercial Weldery," *A.S.M.E. Advance Paper*, N48-A92 for meeting November 29–December 3, 1948.

Ogden, J. O., "Production of Machine Frames by Electric Arc," *Instn. Production Engineers Journal*, Vol. 21, No. 5 (May 1942).

Oldenkamp, H. A., "Welded Design as Applied to Light Weight Army and Navy Structures," *Welding Journal*, Vol. 25, No. 1 (January 1946).

Oliver, F. J., "Machine Housings Welded to Close Limits," *Iron Age*, Vol. 140, No. 2 (July 1937).

Osgood, C. C., "Investigation of Lateral Distortion Produced in Mild Steel Plates by Oxyacetylene Cutting," *Welding Journal*, Vol. 22, No. 7 (July 1943).

Owens, J. W., "Arc Welding," *Metals and Alloys*, Vol. 19, No. 1 (January 1944).

————, "Evolution of Diesel Engine Block Weldment Design and Fabrication," *Welding Journal*, Vol. 26, No. 3 (March 1947).

————, "Routine Inspection and Salvage of Defective Machinery Weldments," *Steel*, Vol. 115, No. 20 (November 1944).

Pellett, D. L., "Complete Redesign Required for Welded Construction," *Machine Design*, Vol. 4, No. 11 (November 1932).

Powers, E. C., "Arc Welding Promotes Evolution in Design," *Machine Design*, Vol. 10, No. 3 (March 1938).

Reisser, S. M., "Fabricated Machine Construction," *Instn. Production Engrs. Journal*, Vol. 17, No. 11 (November 1938).

Richards, L. O., "Welded Engine Base Proves to Be Better than Cast Iron," *Welding Engineer*, Vol. 24, No. 8 (August 1939).

Rindal, R. R., "Shop Set-up for Fabrication of Welded Machinery," *Welding Journal*, Vol. 12, No. 11 (November 1933).

Rockefeller, H. S., "Improved Methods of Machine Flame Cutting," *Welding Journal*, Vol. 22, No. 2 (February 1943).

Ros, M., and A. Eichinger, "The Strength of Welded Connections," *Iron and Steel Institute, Symposium on the Welding of Iron and Steel*, London, Vol. 2 (1935), p. 843.

Russell, P. A., "Cast Iron and Its Relation to Machine Tools," *Instn. Production Engrs. Journal*, Vol. 19, No. 4 (April 1940). Also *Foundry Trade Journal*, Vol. 46, No. 1230 (March 1940).

Semper, E. S., and L. J. Hancock, "Plate Edge Preparation for Welding," *Inst. Welding Trans.*, April 1946.

Sherman, W. F., "Welded Machine Base Fabrication," *Iron Age*, Vol. 140, No. 8 (August 1937).

Slottman, G. V., "Methods for Controlling Plate Motion during Flame Cutting Operations," *American Machinist*, Vol. 89, No. 21 (October 21, 1945).

———, "Stack Cutting of Thin Sheets Produces Parts of Identical Contour," *American Machinist*, November 1945.

Smith, E. W. P., "Welded Construction," *Product Engineer*, Vol. 13, No. 7 (July 1932).

Smith, M. C., "Welded Construction Affects Economies," *Product Engineer*, Vol. 1, No. 8 (August 1930).

Smythe, J. F., "Flame Cutting," *Steel*, January 1946.

Snyder, G. L., "Design Considerations for Welding Machinery Parts," *A.S.M.E. Advance Paper*, No. 45, A62, 1945.

———, "Designing Welded Machinery Parts," *Welding Journal*, Vol. 25, No. 2 (February 1946).

Solakian, A. G., "Stresses in Transverse Fillet Welds by Photoelastic Methods," *Welding Journal*, Vol. 13, No, 2 (February 1934).

Spackman, G. D., "Light Weight Rigid Welded Base on Kingsbury Drilling Machine," *Welding Journal*, Vol. 15, No. 3 (March 1936).

Stone, M., and J. G. Ritter, "Electrically Welded Structures Under Dynamic Stress," *Journal of the American Institute of Electrical Engineers*, Vol. 49, No. 3 (March 1930).

Sykes, F. W., "Design For Welding," *Industry and Welding*, Vol. 17, No. 7 (July 1944).

Tangerman, E. J., "Arc Welding," *American Machinist*, Vol. 75, No. 1 (July 1931).

Thomas, B. S., "Structural Steel Replaces Castings in This Plant," *Industry and Welding*, Vol. 6, No. 3 (September 1933).

Thomas, J. V., "Combined Forming and Cutting Operations in Welding," *Machinery* (London), Vol. 63, No. 1619 (October 1943).

Tyrie, T., "Cast Iron for Modern Engineering Application," *Foundry Trade Journal*, February 22, 1929, and March 7, 1940.

Van Doren, H. L., "Designing for Appearance," *Machine Design*, Vol. 7, No. 2 (February 1935).

Verson, H., "Welded Steel in Heavy Machinery," *Welding Engineer,* Vol. 22, No. 2 (February 1937).

Vogel, A., "Design of Joints for Welded Steel Structures," *Welding Journal,* Vol. 8, No. 4 (April 1929).

Warren, W. H., "Rational Design as Applied to Mill Housings," *Iron Age,* Vol. 131, No. 12 (March 1933).

Waters, D. V., "Welded Construction Applied to Special Machinery," *Product Engineer,* Vol. 2, No. 4 (April 1931).

Weaver, J. R., "Machine Tool Frames Produced By Welding," *Machinery,* Vol. 38, No. 3 (November 1931).

Weiskopf, W. A., and M. Mah, "Stress Distribution in Side Welded Joints," *Welding Journal,* Vol. 9, No. 9 (September 1930).

Westbrook, F. A., "Flame Planer Speeds Plate Edge Preparation," *Machine Tool Blue Book,* May 1946.

White, R. B., "How and Where to Use Welded Fabrication," *Machine Design,* Vol. 13, No. 4 (April 1941).

Wilhelm, F. J., "Simplified Designs Using Standard Structural Shapes," Vol. 24, No. 8 (August 1939).

Wills, C. A., "Welded Rolled Steel Design for Iron and Steel Industry," *Welding Journal,* Vol. 11, No. 9 (September 1932).

Wolf, R. I., and C. Eiwen, "Design of Welded Parts," *Product Eng.,* Vol. 17, No. 7 (July 1946).

Wyer, R. F., "Automatic Arc Welding Solves Production Problems," *Welding Journal,* Vol. 23, No. 2 (February 1944).

Yarrow, R., "Check Your Machine Flame Cutting Procedures," *Industry and Welding,* June 1947.

"Code for Fusion Welding and Gas Cutting in Building Construction," The American Welding Society, 33 West 39th St., New York.

"Fusion-Welded Pressure Vessels," *Technical Report,* British Boiler and Insurance Co., Ltd., 1928, pp. 26–28.

"Report of the Structural Steel Welding Committee of the American Bureau of Welding," The American Welding Society, 33 West 39th St., New York, 1931.

"Tentative Code for Fusion Welding and Flame Cutting in Machinery Construction," The American Welding Society, 33 West 39th St., New York.

"Welding and Cutting Nomenclature, Definitions and Symbols," The American Welding Society, 33 West 39th St., New York.

BOOKS

Air Reduction Sales Company, *Manual of Design for Arc Welded Steel Structures,* New York, Air Reduction Sales Company, 1947.

American Foundrymens Association, *Cast Metals Handbook,* Chicago, American Foundrymens Association, 1944 ed.

American Society for Metals, *Metals Handbook,* Cleveland, American Society for Metals, 1939.

American Welding Society, *A.W.S. Welding Handbook*, New York, American Welding Society, 1942 ed.

Boston, O. W., *Metal Processing*, New York, John Wiley & Sons, Inc., 1941.

Bradford, L. J., and P. B. Eaton, *Machine Design*, New York, John Wiley & Sons, Inc., 5th ed., 1947.

Brooking, W. J., *Arc Welding Engineering and Production Control*, New York, McGraw-Hill Book Company, Inc., 1944.

Berard, S. J., and E. O. Waters, *Elements of Machine Design*, New York, D. Van Nostrand Company, Inc., 2d ed., 1932.

Campbell, H. L., *Metal Castings*, New York, John Wiley & Sons, Inc., 1936.
————, *The Working, Heat Treating, and Welding of Steel*, New York, John Wiley & Sons, Inc., 2d. ed., 1940.

Chase, H., *Handbook on Designing for Quantity Production*, New York, McGraw-Hill Book Company, Inc., 1944.

Faires, V. M., *Design of Machine Elements*, New York, The Macmillan Company, rev. ed., 1941.

Guillet, George L., *Kinematics of Machines*, New York, John Wiley & Sons, Inc., 1940.

Hyland, P. H., and J. B. Kommers, *Machine Design*, New York, McGraw-Hill Book Company, Inc., 3rd ed., 1943.

Jefferson, T. B., *Welding Encyclopedia*, Chicago, Welding Engineer Publishing Company, 11th ed., 1943.

Leutwiler, O. A., *Elements of Machine Design*, New York, McGraw-Hill Book Company, Inc., 1917.

Lincoln Electric Co., *Arc Welding, The New Age in Iron and Steel*, Cleveland, The Lincoln Electric Co., 1928.

Lincoln Electric Co., *Procedure Handbook of Arc Welding Design and Practice*, Cleveland, The Lincoln Electric Co., 8th ed., 1945.

Linde Air Products Co., *Oxy-acetylene Handbook*, New York, The Linde Air Products Co., 15th ed., 1939.

Mackenzie, L. B., *The Welding Encyclopedia*, Chicago, The Welding Engineer Publishing Co., 15th ed., 1943.

Mahla, E. M., and G. E. Doan, *Principles of Physical Metallurgy*, New York, McGraw-Hill Book Company, Inc., 2d ed., 1941.

Marks, L. S., *Mechanical Engineers' Handbook*, New York, McGraw-Hill Book Company, Inc., 4th ed., 1941.

Owens, J. W., *Fundamentals of Welding*, Cleveland, Penton Publishing Company, 1923.

Penton Publishing Company, *Foundrymens Handbook*, Cleveland, Penton Publishing Company, 1923.

Priest, H. M., *Practical Design of Welded Steel Structure*, New York, American Welding Society, 1943.

Rossi, B. E., *Welding and Its Application*, New York, McGraw-Hill Book Company, Inc., 1941.

Spotts, Merkyle Franklin, *Design of Machine Elements*, New York, Prentice-Hall, Inc., 1948.

Vallance, A., and V. L. Doughtie, *Design of Machine Members*, New York, McGraw-Hill Book Company, Inc., 1943.

Index